D0489979

REAR COLUMNS

Collected Diaries
of the Famous

For Teddy St Aubyn

Published in Great Britain
by Private Eye Productions Ltd
6 Carlisle Street, London W1V 5RG
in association with Corgi Books

© 1992 Pressdram Ltd
ISBN 0 552 13995 5

Designed & illustrated by Bridget Tisdall
Cover montage by Nick May
Cover photos © REX
Printed in Great Britain by
The Bath Press, Bath, Avon

Corgi Books are published by Transworld Publishers Ltd
61-63 Uxbridge Road, Ealing, London W5 5SA
in Australia by Transworld Publishers (Australia) Pty, Ltd
15-23 Helles Avenue, Moorebank, NSW 2170
and in New Zealand by Transworld Publishers (N.Z.) Ltd
Cnr Moselle and Waipareira Avenues, Henderson, Auckland

REAR COLUMNS

Collected Diaries of the Famous

EDITED BY CRAIG BROWN

PRIVATE EYE · CORGI

Craig Brown writes two columns a week for *The Times*, another two for the *Sunday Times*, and one for the *Independent on Sunday*. He is the author of *The Marsh Marlowe Letters* (1984), *A Year Inside* (1988), a collection of his parliamentary sketches, and *The Agreeable World of Wallace Arnold* (1990).

"Many of the mad derelicts you encounter out of doors, barking at strangers in the street or trumpeting generalised rage and pain on top of buses, were poets and politicians who were lured by Craig Brown into close-quarters duffing-up."

William Donaldson, The Independent

FOREWORD
by HRH The Prince of Wales

I have long maintained that a special medal should be struck for that wise gentleman who coined the phrase "variety is the spice of life".

Wherever I go at home and abroad, I am often tremendously struck by the varieties of different people there are. People of all colours, shapes and sizes, yes, but also people with very different ways of looking at things.

Yet in many ways there is more that makes us all similar than makes us different. For instance, most of us have the same number of hands, feet, eyes, and so on, and quite a number of us are lucky to live in a house or houses.

I remember Sir Laurens van der Post saying as we were looking out to sea that deep down the Bushmen of the Kalahari are really not so very different from the Members of Lloyds. This was some time ago. Now, of course, the Bushmen might be rather better off than the Lloyds Members, but Sir Laurens's point still holds.

Which brings me to this book, written by some very remarkable individuals, including, I might add, some of my own close relations!

Private Eye magazine has made quite a name for jokes, "gossip" and spoofs, but lot of people forget that for the past few years it has also carried a more reflective and serious "Diary" page. This has allowed people in the public eye the 'right of reply', giving them a fair crack of the whip to put across their particular point of view in their own particular way.

For me, it is a welcome breath of fresh air from what one might call the negativity that can sometimes hamper the rest of the magazine. I hope in future the Editor and his staff might also consider running a regular page on all the marvellous things that are going on in different communities up and down the country.

Until then, this book provides much food for thought. I was fascinated to read, for instance, Mr Peter Mayle's marvellous pen-portrait of life in Provence, an area in many ways reminiscent of the Kalahari.

Fascinating, too, was the present Archbishop of Canterbury's thoughtful piece on bringing Christianity to the young by employing youthful performers such as Cliff Richard and Cliff Michelmore to "get the message cross", as it were.

And my own grandmother, HRH Queen Elizabeth the Queen Mother, reveals her affection for the ordinary, decent Cockneys with whom she keeps in touch via the popular television series *Neighbours*.

So – plenty of reading ahead, and one or two light-hearted "Neddy Seagoon" type jokes along the way from splendid comedians such as that first-class American punster Gore Vidal and his equally amusing kinsman, the television comic Clive James.

As I said at the start of this introduction, collections such as this go to prove two things: that deep down we are all very different, and that at the profoundest level we are all very much the same. I think it was my friend Sir Laurens van der Post who said, "It takes all sorts". These are words I have found myself recalling time and time again as I read this book.

Charles

Gloucester • Berneray • Kalahari
Cornwall • Madrid • London
May–September 1992

JANET STREET-PORTER

Completely bloody brilliant or grooverama as my live-in boyfriend Normski might say. I just came back from the United States of America — United States of Arseholes, more like, when you see what they're doing against the duly elected democratic government of President Ortega in El Salvador, talk about grimsville — where I managed to sign up some of the most brilliantly faberoso new programmes around.

I don't want to come over all hoity-toity, no way, but I just happen to be the Head of Youth Progs at the Beeb, and I don't want to appear stuck up about it but I've bloody well revolutionised the mid-evening output on the screens four-days-a-bloody-week. Talk about boring, the other department heads are so *square* they still think Kenneth Kendall is where it's at. Nerd off, I feel like saying to them, don't you geezers realise that the hippest place in the planet is not Shepherds Bush but Ameri-fuckin-ca? Rap music, Andy Warhol, dark glasses, Adidas trainers, sports cars — they're the latest thing around, and they all come out of what we in the know call the Big Apple.

So anyway, I come back from America armed with a whole range of progies that are going to knock you literally sideways they're so gear. TV just won't be the same again, no way José, not after you see what we got. Here's the Spring list of the ultra-faberooni progs upcoming on a set at a squat near you — *The Man from Uncle* (episodes 25–56), *Mission Impossible* (fourth series), *The Very Best of The High Chapparal* and *The Andy Williams Half Hour (1968–75)*.

Are the greysuits at the Beeb ready for this rap, I ask myself? Probably not, but stuff 'em guys — let's groovebag!

Current fave rave smash craze-ups: potato croquette sandwiches on rye with prawn, a short black brocade sheath with triple shoulder straps and a marabou feather trim from the completely brilliant Azzedine Alaia, massive great canvases full of blacks, browns and kind of blacky-browns by this great new Aborigine post-punk artist I discovered in Manchester, shoe-horns (as is well known, I have a collection plastered into the ceiling of my bedroom), my boyfriend Normski (of course!), his little brothers Gormski, Dormski and Bormski, who're incidentally the best rappers I've heard all month, the latest totally brill CD by the Pet Shop Boys and, for snax, baked beans served on cocktail stix covered in a white choccy sauce — scrumerooni per favor!

Talk about tragic. The Head Squares at the Beeb have just admitted they've never even heard of The Sauerkraut 3 Featuring Perkin X. "They're only number 5 in this week's RAP 'N' TOSS magazine's disco playlist, but don't let that bother you!" I say sarcastically. I'm in the process of arguing that it's about bloody time they had more rap on stuffy snootsville programmes like *Newsnight* instead of all them men in suits talking out their arses 'bout nothin' in 'articular. In my humble opinion, Normski would make a far more in presenter than Peter Snow, who frankly just don't have the rhythm. "And another thing," I say, when they shake their grey heads. "All the kids I know are sick up to their arseholes with that Major bloke monopolising the news programmes all bloody time. They want more of Magenta and Sankha and Antoine, people with gloves, people who know what to do with lycra, people with a bit of style, for Christ's sake!" And do they listen? Not bloody likely. Tragic.

I guess you could say I'm a bit of a rebel. Let me throw a few for instances at you. Like, when I go for munchies at The Savoy, I refuse to wear a fur coat, I'm sorry I just do. Also, my spectacles are tinted and unlike most other people in top jobs, I think it's high time this country got rid of that bloody woman Thatcher as Prime Minister, I mean this poll tax is just absurd. And when I give a dinner party, I have been known to tell my guests to sit wherever they want, none of this man, woman, man, woman lark, and also if it's soup I say let's not bother with soup-spoons, let's just use any old spoons. Yeah, rebel is my middle name, and sometimes I think I know how Malcolm X (my mega-tip for '92) must have felt. I guess that's why I was asked to deliver the address at this year's Female Persons In The Media Luncheon at the Café Royal last week. Talk about going to bloody town. I wore my £1,500 Junior Gaultier lycra go-go top with my £850 A La Mode waistcoat and a dishy little £1,650 Hamnett wraparound skirt number and I looked fan-tastic as I got out my fave Mercedes with its crazy personalised numberplate (JSP1 — my initials) and swung through those doors. The theme of my address? "Street Cred: An End to the Consumer Society As We Know It". I guess it might not

have been what they wanted to hear, but too bad. Anti-establishment? You betcha, babe.

You should see Normski and JSP1 groovin' down the clubs to all the latest sounds around. We sure know where it's at, and where it's at is at downtown Boogieville, shakin' our bodies and lettin' it all hang out to all the latest hip-hop bops on the turntable. Faaaar out! Of course, when I boogie on down to clubland, I take my professional eyes with me, 'cos I'm always on the look-out for revolutionary new talent and style trends for all the completely brilliant new projex I got lined up for my forthcoming Youth Progs. Then I write up the latest buzzes on the street in my BBC notebook under "WOT'S HOT", including "MEGA-HIP WORDZ AND XPRESSIONS" and I make bloody sure they're featured on the next upcoming Youth Prog, okay?

You want xamples? Like, the last time Normski and JSP1 strutted to the mega-mega-monster sounds at the Bubblehouse in Brixton, I wrote these notes on four of the very latest most swingiest catchphrases the totally hip can hear down the klubz these days. Don't ask me what they mean, but they're hot, they're in, they're totally brilliant and I overhead them all:

1. "Move Over, Gran."
2. "Wot-a-Frite."
3. " 'Oo's the OAP?"
4. "44 Minimum."

After the completely unreal success of my infotainment prog named after the catchword "DEFII", I'm thinking of calling the mega follow-up "44MIN". Kinda katchy and kurrent, huh, and so wot if it means nuthin to the middle-class and the middle-aged? Frankly, love, they're not wot I'm about, not at aaall, man.

SENATOR EDWARD KENNEDY

May I say this through the offices of your great journal to all our friends in the Soviet Union. Great cities, great countries, great nations, can be destroyed in a brief moment of time. I remember as a United States senator visiting Beirut when she was a strong, beautiful, proud city. Soon after, she was in ruins. I made a whistle-stop tour of the great city of Addis Ababa. I left it in ruins. I was welcomed to South Africa when she was the shining pearl of that great continent. Within days, she had been ravaged. There is a lesson to be learned here by us all. When we have discovered for ourselves what exactly it is, our children will be able to rest easy in their beds. I know you will be glad to hear that I hope to pay an official visit to the Soviet Union as soon as possible.

The events at Chappaquiddick are now water under the bridge. As a nation, we must learn to look ahead. The future lies dependent not on our past; nor does it lie dependent upon our present: our future is dependent upon our present lies. My advisers, my friends, my family, my medical officers, my probation officers, and the people of Massachussetts have urged me to wait another thirty years before putting myself forward for the most honorable of offices, the Presidency of the United States of America. In the year 2021, I will still be only eighty-eight years of age, still young enough to put my name forward — if this be the will of the nation. By this time Chappaquiddick will seem like the merest splash in the ocean.

Let me say one thing to you straight down the line. You cannot go through an ordeal such as I suffered last Easter without making up your own mind that in future you are going to be more attentive to behavior. And this I vow with all the solemnity at my disposal: when next I sink a bottle and a half, okay, three-quarters, of Scotch, hey, did someone mention Scotch?, woohoo count me in guys, I will on no account whatsoever allow my judgement to interfere with my behavior correction my behavior to interfere with correction my interfering behavior to be judged by the mass media, say, Carl, could you work on this and get it right by the morning? I'm kinda tired.

Straightaway, let me take this opportunity to discountenance any rumors which may or may not be circulating that I am no longer in close touch with my wife Joan Jane Jan Jean could someone check on that name please? Kennedy. We are legally divorced and though we do not see one another or speak to one another we remain in close touch for the sake of our marriage, and of our family, and of the American people. I have the greatest respect and admiration for the great spirit of independence of my wife Mrs Kennedy. She has long been a great tonic to my family and hers, to our family, a great tonic, joan and tonic, say, yeah, sure thing, I could sink one of those, slice of lemon, straight up, on the rocks but let me make one thing clear our marriage is not on the rocks now nor was it ever either before or after our legal divorce. When you enter politics, you know there's going to be the media to deal with, you know you're just not going to be let off easy, but, hell, that's just one of the risks, the whisks, the whiskies. Chivas Regal, why not, that you make for the greater good of mankind. Thank you kindly for your attention.

$\mathbf{W}$e have been called America's First Family. I'll admit that has a nice ring to it. To me, the basis of American life still lies in binge-drinking correction the family. If I have made a mistake in my life — a life I am proud to have dedicated to the service of our great democracy — it could be that I have failed to allow the American people a full enough understanding of the very real love we Kennedys experience when we get together around the blaze of the old log fire.

Picture it now if you will, a typical night at my cosy homestead on Ocean Boulevard. Over in the corner, my son Kennedy J.F. Kennedy, who has always struggled to stay out of the limelight, is hard at work stacking his syringes, he was always a tidy boy, a credit to his family. "Hey paw," he says, his eyes blazing the color of the most perfect Mediterranean sunset. "The fire's goin' out", so I chuck some more evidence on to it, and it glows great once more for one brief shining moment.

$\mathbf{I}$n another corner sits my dear old mother, Rose Kennedy, one hundred and one years young and still applying lipstick to her face all day, every day. "Sing us one of your ballads, Jack," she says. "Ted," I say. "Ted," she says. "Sing us one of your lovely ballads, Ted." She warms to the haunting Irish ballads of our forefathers such as "The Road To The Isles", "Men Of Harlech", Dick O'Van Dyke's "Chim-Chim-Cheroo" and "Tie Me Kangaroo Down, Sport" by Eire's proudest son, Rolf O'Harris.

As my lungs fill with the song of my ancestors, watched over by my niece Edwina Bobby Kennedy Kennedy and her children Ken-Ken Kennedy, K. Enid-Di Kennedy and Neddy-Ken Kennedy Jr, with tears swelling in my eyes I think of the torch of truth it has been my burden to shoulder throughout my adult life. "A sweep is as lucky as lucky can be," I chorus, and it chokes me to think of the torment and hardship I have undergone as a senior Senator from America's first family, nearly crushed  by the burden of massive wealth. This, I think, gives me a unique understanding of the pain my forebears were forced to suffer in the famous Irish Potato Famine of 18 er 18 could someone check that date please? "Then blow me a kiss — and that's lucky too!" I draw the lilting ballad to an end, and when I look up frankly there isn't a dry eye in the house. In fact there isn't anyone at all in the house — they've all gone down to the Copacabana on Main Street.

$\mathbf{A}$s part of the Kennedy clan, I have felt it my noble duty to pick up the women the torch passed on to me by others, to rededicate myself to the freedom of the people and their longing for a better future and to reach out and touch whoever's panting for it the very hearts and minds of our common humanity. The very values which we all share — peace on earth, economic growth at home, compassion to all our fellow Americans — are the values I personally hold most dear. That enough? Great, and not a single mention of Kopechne.

REV IAN PAISLEY MP

Before breakfast the other morning, I noticed that my new toothbrush, purchased by my good wife on the day previous, bore the legend, "Manufactured in Italy". My horror was indeed a thing to behold.

"The Whore of Rome has entered into my very mouth!" I cried above the sizzle and crackle of eggs frying. "The Harlot has ridden her beastie into my very pinkest of cavities! Begone, foul bristles!" So saying, I hurled the Scarlet Brush into the depth of our God-fearing toilet and flushed and flushed with all my might and vigour until the iniquitous Anti-Christ was but a memory.

"The enemy hath been vanquished," I informed my wife Eileen as I took up my seat and walked with it to the breakfast table. "Let us now to grace."

Eileen bent her head low as I addressed the Almighty prior to mastication. "Almighty God, You sent Your only Son to earth so that Ulster may be free and the deceits of the Fenians may be routed with a sword. Have mercy on us as we eat of this nutritious Protestant food. May our enemies suffer thine arrows and may this sausage which I now ravage on Your behalf aid me to see You in Heaven together with Good King William and one or two other members of my church and Yours where we shall rejoice to observe below us the successive Whores of Rome burning in Hell Fire. Amen."

As I placed the sausage in my mouth, a rasping noise of great volume issued from the seat of my pants.

"Oh, Ian!" exclaimed Eileen, opening a window to let the fair winds blow. "If the trumpet give an uncertain sound, who shall prepare himself to battle?" I replied, and with that we heard no more of the matter.

Thought for the Day (1): Let not spaghetti into your larder, nor pasta into your pot. Check first thine noodles that they be manufactured in the domain of Her Majesty. Beware products named Dolmio, for the Scarlet Sauce is touched by the hand of Satan.

Time and time again, I have expressed myself willing to fight for unity amongst the good people of Ulster. I have entered the so-called Peace Talks of Mr So-Called Brooke with an open mind, determined to abject myself before the twin monsters of reconciliation and harmony. But time and time again I have seen these good wishes thwarted by a callous disregard of Christian sensitivities.

"Pray what, sir, do you mean by this?" I demanded of Mr Babbling Brooke as we assembled around the table for our first discussion. "This is no good, no good at all. This table, sir, is entirely the wrong shape. It is a deliberate insult to the loyal people of Ulster, nothing else!"

"B-b-b-but," he said, "it's a round table."

"Precisely my point, sir!" I exclaimed. "The shape of the rosary bead and of the pontiff's cap, the shape of the communion wafer and of the cardinal's fingernail, the shape of a united Ireland and of the dome of St Peter's Church in Babylon! Gentlemen, we have been deceived! Let these discussions continue not one second more!"

"B-b-b-but," replied Brooke, "they haven't yet started."

"Nor will they, sir! And let me tell you this! Until this unholy insult of a table is removed and destroyed in its entirety there will be no Peace in Ulster!"

It is clear beyond the shadow of a doubt that Brooke and his minions have not the slightest intention to see justice for the people of Ulster. Not until he builds us a good, square, small Protestant table with room for just one man's throne behind it will I ever believe that he intends to allow Ulster the government for which she craves. No surrender!

*T*hought for the Day (2): "Love Thy Neighbour." What did Jesus Christ *mean* by this precisely? Focus your attention, if you will, on that word "L-O-V-E". What, you might ask, did he mean by *that*? Would this man who came with a sword to rid us of our enemies ever renege on his quest for violence with such a wishy-washy word? No, no, no and thrice no. The explanation is in fact simple. Rearrange the letters and you will find revealed, as though by the light of a burning torch, the word "V-O-L-E", i.e. "Vole thy Neighbour as thyself." The vole — one of the original inhabitants, I need not remind you, of Noah's great Ark — is a ratlike rodent much given to digging and burying. Thus the word of the Lord is revealed! And I say unto you, "Bury Thy Neighbour!" Bury Him for the Lord! Hallelujah! Hallelujah!

*P*rivately, I am, I confess, an amusing, charming and tolerant fellow, with a warmth that belies my public image. I am known, too, for my Christian kindness to the irrelevant little people who work for me and look up to me as a man of force and destiny. Mr James Molyneaux, for instance, I always allow to be by my side, carrying my briefcase and my Bible. In return I allow him to offer me his wholesale devotion. If ever he forgets his place, I bring him back to earth — for his own sake — by cracking one of my good-hearted jokes! "Funny you never married, Jim!" I like to bellow whenever we are together in a room full of people, and poor Jim goes red, almost scarlet, pursing his lips and flickering his eyelashes! Everyone then enjoys a good belly-laugh. This allows us to proceed with the business of the day without fear of contradiction. Jim, too, always welcomes the joke, contemplating it in silence for many an hour, a constant witness to the Messenger of the Lord beside whom he is proud to be seated.

*T*hought for the Day (3): Almighty God appeared to me in a dream last night and he said, Come, Ian Richard Kyle Paisley, come with Me and I shalt show you My dominions. And I went with the Almighty, and He showed me His dominions, strengthened by fire and tempered by wrath. And in His dominions the Protestant was able to do battle with the Catholic for eternity, and the snares of ecumenism were averted. And the Almighty saith unto me, Son Ian, Come sup with Me at My table. And I prepared to be seated. "Sit!" saith the Almighty, and I sat, and thereupon I felt a sharp sword — the sword of Vengeance — enter my Behind, fixing me forever to my seat. And as I sat there, the Lord cackled, declaring that I should now Sup with Him for Eternity. At least, I think it was the Lord...

NIGEL DEMPSTER

It's been another outstanding year of exclusive revelations for the *Mail* Diary — the page that makes compulsory reading for my old friend international playboy and Argentinian jet-setter Luis "The Bounder" Basualdo, 47, glamorous Princess Michael of Kent, 36, and former secretary to former husband of former escort to a former doyenne of the Ipswich business scene Helen Wilkes, 29, and many others — and I can now reveal that I have exclusively outscooped my so-called "rivals" throughout this outstanding year of exclusive revelations.

In January, I burst into the New Year with an exclusive revelation about Lord Lucan, 57, the moustachioed Old Etonian playboy Earl and former member of the Claremont Club, who went missing in 1974 after murdering his former nanny, Sandra Rivett, 32, at the home of his former wife, Jane, 42. Sources close to the errant Earl exclusively reveal to me that he is still missing. "No one has seen him for a very long time," declares a close friend and former aide, who adds: "It's a very long time since he has been seen by anyone." It is now many years since the Earl was last spotted, I reveal.

I hear from my old friend first cousin to the Queen Royal Photographer former man about town restaurateur Patrick Lichfield, 51, that he is planning to stay at home and maybe watch a little television tonight rather than fly in Concorde to Manhattan to have dinner — at an exclusive restaurant once frequented by Ivana Trump, 43, former wife of former husband Donald Trump, 49. "I never fly by Concorde — and to be honest I haven't heard of the restaurant," reveals Patrick, 53, who is a first cousin to the Queen, "so there wouldn't be much point even if I could afford it."

In March, my story of the forthcoming marriage of a former Bristol nightclub owner to the former personal assistant to a former close friend of a former Royal equerry is belatedly picked up by all my so-called "rivals" — even though the story is of no interest to anyone. In the same month — March — I reveal that close friends of Princess Michael of Kent are urging her to devote less of her time to looking after others — and more to herself. "She is terribly kind — much too kind — and never ever thinks of herself. Her life is spent in one charity work after another," Princess Michael dictates to me over the phone that morning. "And she gives what little money she earns to those less fortunate than herself. Be a poppet and give it the lead, Nigel, darling."

I am often asked how I come by so many outstanding revelations. I am giving away no secrets when I reveal that I am of the same class, background and education as the people I feature on my page — and this makes it easy for me to speak to them on a one-to-one basis. It will be a long time before my so-called "rivals" realise that only when one is born into the privileged world of minor public-school Australian-born social-climbing PR executives can one begin to understand them and write about them day after day.

In July, I reveal that Anthony Andrews, 44, has been spotted eating with his wife in a fashionable Battersea restaurant — only to be personally contacted by *Brideshead* actor Anthony Andrews and asked to make it clear that the Anthony Andrews who had been spotted eating with his wife in a fashionable Battersea restaurant was not the *Brideshead* actor Anthony Andrews — but former Kent property developer Anthony Andrews, 67, and his wife June, 58 — whose daughter Lucinda, 24, recently gave birth to a baby boy, Thomas — her second. Husband Maidstone-based former air traffic controller Keith, 35, is reported to be "delighted" — but as yet the couple have "no plans" to take the new baby to Castle Howard — home of the Howard family — to see where Yorkshire TV's *Brideshead Revisited* was originally filmed.

I can exclusively reveal that just sixteen months after attractive, lissome, tireless charity worker and avid art connoisseur Lady "Bubbles" Rothermere, 36, wife of *Daily Mail* proprietor Lord Rothermere, 42, suffered some slight toothache, all is well again. "I can now devote my energies exclusively to my charity work — thanks to my excellent dentist, New Zealand-born John Wainwright, 46 — whose sister former nurse Lorraine, 36, recently managed to book an upper circle seat for Andrew Lloyd Webber's top-rated long-running hit musical *Starlight Express* at the Victoria Palace," says highly regarded society beauty Lady Rothermere, 34, who exclusively reveals that her favourite colour this season is mauve, "or green, depending".

In October, I exclusively reveal that on the death of the present Queen, Belgravia-based former Princess Elizabeth, her eldest son former Naval officer Charles, 42 — close friend of former Goon Harry Secombe, 64 — stands to inherit the throne. This may come as a shock to his younger brother, Andrew, 29 — whose one-time girlfriend actress Katie Rabbett, 27, is currently starring in BBC TV's *You Rang, M'Lud?* on Sunday nights and who may well, she confides, have a baby — "but only after I become pregnant," she insists.

Since establishing myself as *the* leading social historian married to Lady Camilla Dempster, 46, whose great-aunt, Gladys, 91, is the former escort of a close confidant of the former personal assistant to legendary interior designer Hon. Offy Squinks, member of the famous Squinks family of up-and-coming Willesden — I find myself invited to more upper-class parties than I can possibly attend. Yet attend I must, so as not to disappoint my very dear old family friends the aristocracy nor my eight and a half million former readers. For example — today I fit into my packed schedule The Rumbelows PLC Pro-Celebrity Charity Ping-Pong Tournament at Mayfair's Grosvenor House with roly-poly funster Christopher Biggins and effervescent Bonnie Langford in attendance —and the Mike Read/Tim Rice All-Star Charity Roller Disco exclusively catered by Lady Elizabeth Anson, 54, first cousin to the Queen.

PS: My personal guarantee for the New Year — in 1992 Dempster's Diary will continue to bring you all the stories they won't print elsewhere!

ROBERT ROBINSON

A Mr Eric Blessed — blessed name, indeed, one might be forgiven for thinking, albeit a trifle impishly — writes to me from his homestead in Hornchurch, Essex. "Come *off* it, Robinson," he proclaims, a mite injudiciously, I would say. A regular and percipient correspondent, Mr Blessed tackles therein the vexed question of whether one should term the garment worn over one's shirt and under one's sports jacket a *woollie*, a *pullover*, a *jersey*, a *jumper*, or — most controversial of all, some might declare — a *sweater*.

I myself had stuck out my neck in order to proclaim allegiance to *jersey*. Ho hum. Mr Blessed is a sworn *jumper* man, and good for him, but as I perused his letter I found myself delighting in the image of a chap *jumping* up and down, as if in some curious way *becoming* that which he had first sought only to *wear*.

My mind — wayward and eternal student that it is — was soon besieged by other delicious possibilities concerning the inexhaustibly energetic Mr Blessed. Had he, perchance, reacted against other titular labels for said knitted articles of clothing as a result of a peculiarly traumatic experience suffered in youth? Had a policeman once requested the speeding Mr Blessed to *pullover*? Or had Mr Blessed undergone the disappointment — splendid image — of a rainy sojourn

on the fair island of *Jersey*? I would be the last fellow to be so forward as to suggest that our Mr Blessed might ever become perspirant sufficient to be proclaimed a *sweater*, but the mystery holds fast. Personally, I'm rather partial to *jersey*, but there again I must admit that it has been quite an age since I've donned the aforementioned woollen knitwear, preferring a raincoat, which some people choose — for reasons too *bizarre* to contemplate — to call mackintosh.

A **Robinson**: a silly prat, a one-way conversation, or **to robinson**: a verb meaning to pass one's life talking nonsense?

I was wrestling with irresistibly jocular images of the original Mr Mackintosh (was there ever a Mrs Mackintosh, one cannot restrain oneself from wondering?) clad in sou'wester and wellingtons whilst craning my neck (craning! A towering apparatus overhead with a Bert or a Fred at the levers is conjured neatly into one's mind!) towards the ceiling of the Sistine Chapel on a visit to the fair city of Rome recently.

Mr P. T. Hopkinson of Rome had called my attention to the figures of God and Adam thereinupon portrayed — no, no, the word won't do, you don't *portray* God and Adam, you surely some-other-word-I'll-add-in-later them.

Would not Adam, poor chap, have grown the teensiest bit *chilly* lounging around in what we used to delight in terming his birthday suit? All-benevolent being God may well be, but might it not have crossed his mind to slip the shivering fellow a mackintosh or even — heaven forbid — a *jersey*?

Distracted by the sheer *ingenuity* of these fickle thoughts as they fluttered across my mind's eye, I found myself entertaining the suggestion (why, by the by, must one always *entertain* suggestions, as if duty-bound to pass them Dry Martinis and appropriate doilies while they put their feet up on one's sundry furnishings?) that my own *Stop the Week* circle is as close as damnit to the Algonquin Round Table of the 1920s, with Ann Leslie the Dorothy Parker *de nos jours* and Professor Laurie Taylor the Robert Benchley. Might I beg leave to submit that our collected aphorisms ("personally, I've never trusted a woman who wears a bright yellow hat!" — Ann Leslie; "Frankly, Bob, if it's breakfast cereals, I can take them or leave them!" — Professor Laurie Taylor; "In a curious sort of way, a tennis court is ideal for the playing of tennis, but little else!" — R. Robinson) would stand up well in any match against the aforementioned Algonquins?

A **Robert**: A saloon-bar philosopher; a smart-aleck with problem hair; or **to robert** (I robert, you robert, he, she or it roberts): to use thirty words where three would do.

On, or should I say "aboard", a train the other day, I was gently wondering why on earth a motorcar is called a motorcar (what, perchance, is or are a "moto", and what in heaven's name can a "rcar" be?: the mind quite literally boggles) when a ticket-collector came lurching into view.

"Ticket please," he enunciated, hold-ing out a machine which looked for all the world like one of those contraptions great aunts were once in the habit of employing for retrieving stones from the hooves of gee-gees.

"Might I be forgiven for thinking that your over-riding purpose at the present time is to cast a beady eye over my railway ticket, or absence thereof?" I inquired with due geniality.

"Ticket please, sir!" he replied, a mite testily I thought, holding out an ungloved hand for my inspection.

"Come, come, my dear fellow," I said. "A little more *specificity* — if such word exists! — might help matters immeasurably. A ticket to The Proms? A ticket by rickshaw to Timbuctoo? Please define your terms before venturing into such a veritable menagerie of possibilities."

As his clenched fist landed on what I suppose I must learn to call my "hooter", I reflected that all might not be quite right in the baffling world of transport. Alas and alack, my subsequent observation to the incensed collector that he might consider punching my ticket rather than my nasal protuberance resulted in another swift jab, this time to my jaw. Thinking it best to reveal myself in full possession of the travel documentation in question, I was driven to wonder whether the art of conversation is a skill much prized by the modern world.

In which continent would one find a cockatoo? Can you name three Kings of England who have never ventured abroad? What was the former name of Zimbabwe? In what year was the Magna Carta signed? In which opera by Gilbert and Sullivan does Sir Joseph Porter appear? Who or what is a *vizier*? By what quirk of fate did an intelligent human being come to waste his life asking middle-class boffins questions such as these? No conferring.

GLENYS KINNOCK

It's no telly for you, boyo, till you've finished your sums, I told Neil Tuesday last. He's a *Police Academy* nut, says they're hilarious really, and there was one on the telly. But there's no point treating them with kid gloves, honest there's not, and he had all Mr Smith's workings-out for the proposed new Poll Tax to go over, so I pulled out that plug and I said, *Police Academy* can wait, Mr Smith will be ever so cross if you don't mark his sums, he's spent a lot of time on them has Mr Smith, and feet off the table-doily when I'm speaking to you.

Neil's never been one for the sums, but he loves the telly and he's mad about a good curry. "Make mine a Biryani," he says as I nip to the local third world restaurant, and he works up a right old sweat as soon as it's in his mouth. "Could I do with a lager!" he says, nipping to the frigidaire for a four-pack. "Whooooaaah, that's better!"

Tuesday last, with the telly off (and not before time!!) Neil gets out his felt-tip and starts ticking Mr Smith's home-work. He's five minutes in when he looks up with that butter-wouldn't-melt expression and says, "Glen, love, I could murder a Biryani."

Call me a softie, but off I trot, arriving back duly armed with Biryani for His Nibs. What do you know, no sooner have I placed the Biryani on the arm of the easy-chair than whoops, if Neil doesn't knock the blessed thing all over the soft furnishings, drenching Mr Smith's homework in the process. Talk about clumsy! The next day, the Wednesday, he's been spending running through Mr Smith's sums at a press conference. "Boots off!" I say as he came through the door. "And then tell me how it went."

"Just fabulous," he said. "I thought it was going to take one helluva long time and bore me solid but as luck would have it that Biryani stuck the pages together, so no sooner had I finished the first than I was onto the last! We missed out the in between bits — tax and so forth — but who's bothered, eh, love? Ooh, I could murder a lager!"

You'll be wanting to know as to our current bedside reading. Neil's nuts about sci-fi, while I prefer more considered works which keep you abreast of latest developments in women's affairs, the third world and the like. I've read all the books from Richard Attenborough's films, many of them twice. At the moment I am reading the lovely, lovely story of Stompy, a little lad who my good friend Winnie Mandela did everything she could to save from death. She tried yelling at him, clubbing him, beating him, dancing around him, the lot, poor love. And now for her pains she is being prosecuted by the fascist regime in South Africa. Makes you think, eh?

Winnie is always turned out immaculate, as neat as a new pin. But don't talk to Neil about personal cleanliness, he doesn't know the meaning of the word! Of course, he's better now than he was.

When I first met him he would dress any-old-how. He wore Buddy Holly specs but only for show (we're both still tremendous Buddy fans!), scruffy old winklepickers and a dirty leather jacket, with his hair all slicked back in an Elvis quiff. After an exhausting day at Westminster, he still puts on those old winklepickers and the Buddy Holly specs, and he likes to unwind by playing what I believe is known as "dummy guitar" to old favourites like "Peggy Sue" and "That'll Be The Day". After half-an-hour, I tell him enough is enough and I whisk him to the bath for a thorough spring-clean. "Oh, *Glen!*" he sometimes whines, but I tell him that no one wants a dirty boy for Prime Minister, look what happened to Michael Foot. "That Gerald Kauffman is always *very* spruce. Don't tell me *he* doesn't give that face of his a good scrub *at least* twice a day. He's that well-polished, you can see your face in his scalp. And don't forget behind those ears," I add. But does he bother? Does he heck!

I suppose you could call me Neil's political conscience in a manner of speaking. Don't get me wrong, Neil's a smashing lad, really smashing, but for all his energy he sometimes forgets what on earth he's up to and that's when he runs to his Glen. Not so very long ago, when that Nigel Lawson had left in a huff and the job of Chancellor seemed to be going begging, Neil said he was thinking of applying for it, it would be quite a step up, didn't I think, what with a Budget of your own, and it would help my credibility and that. "But *Neil!*" I said to him. "It's a *Conservative* Chancellor they're after, and you're *Labour*! You stand for the *working people* of this country!" "Well," said he. "Businessmen work too, and often very long hours. They need someone to argue their corner, poor loves." "Off to your bath!"

said I. "And not another word!" Result? Application never posted!

Let no one tell me that Neil Kinnock is not a man of principle. We're both still passionately engaging with the same values we fought for when we were first courting. Disarmament, for example. We were both very pro unilateral disarmament, and nowadays we're by no means against it, given the right circumstances, and as long as everyone else does it at roughly the same time. Ditto nationalisation, which we've always felt strongly about. The nitpickers — and there are *always* nitpickers — might say that we were once strongly for it, and we're now strongly *against* it, but let's face it the important thing is that we care one way or the other, which we do, though, frankly, it's hardly worth getting hot under the collar about it either way.

Improve your wordpower: a lot of lovely folk have written in to ask me how Neil gained his tremendous grasp of language. It might surprise them to know that my teaching is by no means confined to the tiny tots! Every day before Neil goes to work, I sit him down, pick up the Family Thesaurus and say a long word like "thoroughly" to which he replies, "Thoroughly completely, absolutely, wholly, unqualifiedly, utterly, totally," and then I give him his biscuits and squash and send him off with a kiss. Come 3, I make myself comfy in front of the telly and watch him condemn the government's latest initiative "completely, absolutely, wholly, unqualifiedly, utterly and totally". It's then that I allow myself a quiet smile. "Glenys," I say, "Glenys, love, there's a man who knows his own mind!"

♥ YOKO ONO ♥

The people of Britain have always felt a strong and spiritual love for Yoko Ono and now Yoko Ono wishes to return that love through the medium of your satirical magazine *Private Eye*. I hope my message will reach into your hearts like grapefruit segments falling from the sky.

Peel an apricot. Place it between your toes. Put on a sock and walk to work. When you arrive, your foot will be very messy, but the sky will still be blue. Yoko Loves You.

Though I am best known as a Conceptual Artist, some people also know that I was once married to John Lennon, the singer. John was really into my art. We met at a show of mine in the Indica Gallery. It was all blank walls except for a small placard saying "EXIT" above a door. He got really into it. It gave him a buzz. "So that's the EXIT, is it?" he joked, and I could tell straight away that we were on the same mystical plane. "Yes," I replied, "that's the EXIT." At that moment, we both knew it was for real.

We were both really into world peace long before it became fashionable. We wrote a beautiful song together called *Give Peas a Chance* because he was really into peas at the time, but I convinced him that Peace and not Peas was where it was at and from that moment on he never campaigned for more peas again. I think that I can now reveal that I re-directed another of his major campaigns too. In 1968, at the height of Vietnam, John asked me to join him in picketing a field of sheep in North Wales with the banner, "Make Love Not Wool". I told him that he had probably misheard, and the rest is history.

John and I were the heroes of a generation, you know. We wrote some of the greatest lyrics of all time together. Remember "Imagine no possessions. It's easy if you try"? We wrote that in our private suite at the New York Hilton during a break while I was administering John's purchase of Real Estate in Arizona and he was organising the purchase of a couple of islands somewhere off the coast of India.

John had a brilliant Liverpudlian wit, and like so many people from the great city of Liverpuddle he was not afraid to use it. Once, when asked by a journalist how he was enjoying living in America, he said, "Fuck off and mind your own business. Screw you, mate!!" Of course, we all fell about with laughter, and the journalist was amazed that a legend such as John could be so frank and so honest and so totally outgoing, and that aphorism of John's has since entered all the anthologies.

On another occasion, he was introduced to the mother of the Queen of England who said, "Are you on tour?" Quick as a flash, using his famous Swiftian surrealist wordplay, John replied, "Not at the moment!!!" Of course, this was not the type of response that The Establishment was used to, but John was a rebel and an anarchist, always speaking the Truth, and that's why he frightened those in positions of power.

Cut a hole in a bed sheet. Put your head through it. Step into a washing machine. Ask your friend to switch it on. Watch the world spin round and round. Step out of the machine. Your bed sheet will still have a hole. Ask your maid to repair it. You are an Artist. Yoko Loves You.

John was a visionary, too. As early as 1966, he was saying that Onions Are Pink Tigers If Only You'll Let Them Be Gear, but in those days hardly anyone believed him. On our shared album, *Yoko and Her Husband Asleep in New York* (1972), he could be heard breathing in his sleep for 23 minutes and 16 seconds, but no one would listen. In 1974, he got into politics in a big way, alerting America and the rest of the world to the danger from Rhododendrons and giving a large sum of money to the agitprop campaign "Blacks Against Manipulation by Rhododendrons". At last the world seemed to sit up and listen, and since that time not a single Rhododendron has been elected to high office in the USA.

Imagine you are a Bernard Matthews Turkey Roast. Climb into a Supermarket Refrigerator and wait to be purchased. When they remove you from the oven, tell them you are an Artist and that Yoko Loves You. Refuse them a refund.

Many people know me by my bottom. As Van Gogh had his ear, so Yoko has her bottom. In fact, I often think that my bottom is the reincarnation of Vincent's ear. It even looks strangely similar. In celebration of this re-birth, I have created a number of exhibits in its honour for my Major Retrospective Exhibition at The Riverside Studios this month. *Bottoms 629* is six hundred and twenty-nine black and white photographs of my bottom taken from unusual angles. *Bottom 1* is another photograph of my bottom in the same series, exhibited in a separate space. *Bicycle Without Bottom* is a plain bicycle standing upright in a

★ STAR THOUGHTS ★
IMELDA MARCOS

It is indeed good that I should be granted asylum and sanctuary for my thoughts and philosophies in what I believe is a magazine of some humour. My late husband, President Ferdinand Marcos, had great humour, and he was much venerated by his nation for his love of laughter. Now when I visit his dear body each week in its beautiful fridge-freezer in the delightful Temples Memorial Park in Florida, I narrate him many jokes. One of his very favourites is:
Question: "When is a door not a door?"
Answer: "When it is open."
That makes Ferdinand Marcos laugh a lot, for, even though he is no longer with us, I employ gloves to move his Presidential lips up and down in the fridge-freezer, indicating that he is responding well to the many jokes from his darling Imelda.

corner, without any photograph of my bottom. Confronting the viewer with an absence of bottom, I ask him to question the very nature of what he once called reality. You know, I remember a reporter once asking John what reality was. John thought hard. "Reality", he announced at last, "is like Reality." Once again, his brutal honesty and visionary genius had unflinchingly revealed the truth.

Love Poem Number 9: Remove your chequebook from your wallet. Write out a cheque made payable to Yoko Ono. Post it to New York. Watch as your cheque becomes Real Estate. And always remember: Yoko Loves You.

THE RT REV GEORGE CAREY

Cheers all round to every reader of this robustly humorous, and, in a very real sense, Christian magazine! You probably don't know me from the proverbial Adam, but this week I put on the smashing new cap of "ArchBee of C". This is what I call myself when communicating with the young (for whom, incidentally, I have a lot of time).

"Communicating". It's an awfully long word, isn't it? And it means a lot too. To my mind, Jesus was the greatest communicator of them all, a sort of olden day disc-jockey, if you like. But instead of the Hit Parade, Jesus had his Top Ten parables, and instead of the phone-in, he had a hotline to God. If there's one thing I want to achieve in my new job, it's to see us playing more of the Top Ten at 45rpm, and less at 33rpm! There's nothing wrong with a bit of get up and go, as Brian Clough once told me!

"Parables". What do we mean by "parables"? That's an awfully tricky word, isn't it? But let's not be frightened by it, because it just means "super stories", much as a splendid modern writer like Jack Higgins or Jeffrey Archer would spin.

I am, by the way, a terrific believer in the modern world. We can all learn a lot from gadgets, and I believe that if Jesus were around today, he would be the first to use the tin-opener, the non-stick frying pan and the sticky label. But  the modern world does create tremendous pressures on the individual, and this is the topic I would like to tackle in this column. Cheers!

First, a little bit about yours truly. Everyone calls me George, and that's the way I like it. I'm a great one for Churches being friendly forums for folk young and old to get together in drama workshops or encounter groups so as to hammer out what makes them tick. Super. When I arrived at Wells Cathedral I thought to myself, "George," I thought, "George, you'll have to do something about this fuddy-duddy old building if you're going to grab the punters by the proverbial lapels — for a start, those crumbly old walls could do with a lick of paint!"

Within a week, I had armed a keen band of young Christian helpers with the requisite brushes, and, singing that fine old Christian hymn "Hey Ho, Hey Ho, It's Off To Work We Go", they soon had those stone walls a cheerful bright orange. Result? Bums on seats went right up, and that, in the modern church, is very much the name of the game.

We then covered up the gloomy old tiles and tombs with a nice bit of eezi-kleen carpeting and some fabulous posters of that marvellous singer Cliff Richard — signed by Cliff himself, no less! This greatly appealed to the young, of course, so much so that we included Cliff's Eurovision winner, *Congratulations*, in our first Christmas service, or "get-together" as I prefer to call it. Result? Bums on seats went through the roof.

We shunted the old font to a corner and installed a very popular coffee, tea and sundry hot beverages machine. We established a super "drop-in" centre for the senior citizens where a dusty old chapel used to be. Finally, we got rid of the old altar. In this way we challenged people to be more committed as Christians in the true sense, placing the focus away from the "never-never" world of Holy Ghosts and suchlike and right back into the here and now and what I call the

"Three F's": Friendliness, Fellowship, and Fifty pence for tea or coffee and a digestive (plain or milk chocolate).

I come from what is called the "Evangelical" wing of the old C of E. "Evangelical" — now that's a funny word, and I should think you're wondering what on earth old George is on about. If I've said it once, I've said it one hundred times: there's no future in petrol-station Christianity — using Sunday to fill the spiritual tank for the week. I'm of the firm belief that Jesus himself kept his tank filled throughout the week — and he kept the coupons too, so that, in time to come, he could cash them in for a fully guaranteed household appliance to help him with his work in this life. And we must strive to do likewise, always showing off our new kettles, tumblers and fondue sets so that those less committed to Christianity will say to themselves, "My, I too must fill up my petrol-tank today and everyday so that soon it will be overflowing and the petrol will quickly spread throughout my neighbourhood, leaving its mark on one and all." So, in a nutshell, this is what we mean by Evangelical: Less of the Pomp and more of the Pump. "Nutshell" — now that's a funny word.

F avourite football club? The Gunners, the Gunners, the Gunners all the way! As is by now well-known, I'm a devoted supporter of Arsenal Football Club. I believe that we in what I call "The Global Christian Business" can learn a lot from their teamwork, energy and general control of the ball. In a funny sort of way, football has a lot in common with true Christianity, you know. For instance, there is only one God, and there is only one football per game. Football goes back years and years, and so of course does God. A

good football is made from stout leather, and so are many Bibles, though in this day and age I often think that a handy paperback Bible is just as good, and much more convenient. Those of us who hope to "score for the Lord" would do well to take a tip from the top Arsenal strikers. When I asked Paul Merson — a great chum of mine — how he performed his magic, he said something that has stayed in my mind to this very day. Do you know what he said? He said, "Keep your eyes on the ball and give it all you got." Plenty of food for thought for all committed Christians there, I would suggest!

R oll up! Roll up! It's time for all Christians in the public eye to stand up and be counted! To me, "telly" can be a potent force for good in our world, as can be seen from the continuing success of such marvellous programmes as *Songs of Praise* and the excellent five-minute *Time for Thought* broadcast at 11.55am every third Tuesday on the Open University course (channels vary). As a way of attracting the young in this Decade of Evangelism, I have formed a "Rock Stars for the Lord" consortium of rock stars who are not Afraid to be Anglican. We already have big-name rock stars such as Cliff Richard, Sir Harry Secombe, Cliff Michelmore and Thora Hird — and if that fabulous line-up won't bring in the young, then frankly I don't know what will!

PETER USTINOV

Welcome to my world. The Queen Mother — and never, whatever you do, underestimate the exceptional acuity of that good lady — once told me over a light but agreeable luncheon that (President) Ronnie Reagan had once said to her that Mikhail Gorbachev, for whom I have much admiration, had described me as "an ambassador of goodwill to all nations", and I humbly hope that some of this charm will enhance the lives of all those who chance upon this page.

I have, I am told, the "gift of the gab". In their kinder moments, my friends accuse me of being an accomplished raconteur. I suppose that I do notice the little things that others, far more illustrious than myself, may overlook.

They accuse me also of being particularly good at accents, of being able to bring a person to life through remarkable powers of mimicry. For instance, I was strolling along the streets of London's Chelsea last week when I noticed a sooty-faced news vendor, shouting, with all the aplomb of his profession, "Read all 'bout it! Lor' luvaduck, blow me down wiv a fevver! Read all 'bout it!"

This young fellow's eyes blazed with enthusiasm as I asked him to supply me with a copy of the *News Chronicle*. "You're a gent, an' no mistake, guv," he beamed as I supplied him with the requisite pennies, "Read all 'bout it! Read all 'bout it! 'Enny, 'enny 'enny ol' iron!"

My actor's eyes and ears, which are, I regret to say, relentlessly active, soaked in his every mannerism, his every word, his every misplaced vowel. I planned to place this charming fellow in the vaults of my imagination, to be brought out to the delight of international audiences — many of them including royalty and world leaders — at some future date. Or should I paint a picture of him? Or create a musical around him? Or bring him to life in an original novel? I am, I'm sorry to admit, lumbered with a grievous number of talents, so much so that I sometimes find it hard to know which to turn to first! Perhaps, I thought, I should seek the advice of the effortlessly charming young "'bloke" from whom I had just purchased my *News Chronicle*.

"Read all 'bout it! Chim-chim-er-nee, Chim-chim-cheroo!" he continued to holler as I approached him once more, his bright blue eyes alive in his grubby face.

"Excuse me, young fellow," I interrupted him. "But I have it in mind to recreate you in a musical, a play, a novel, a short story, on canvas or in an evening of anecdotes. Which, may I ask, would you prefer?"

The cheery young chappie's eyes were ablaze with all the bright luminosity of his cockney forefathers.

"Fuck off, yer smug fat git," he trilled. "Read all 'bout it! Read all 'bout it!"

I remember once, over a rather fine luncheon with Mikhail Gorbachev, telling him how my dear friend the late David Niven had once had cause to introduce me to his old pal John F. Kennedy, who had once awarded me the great compliment of roaring with laughter as I told him of the time I had been entertained to a splendid dinner by

Bertrand Russell and the inimitable Charlie Chaplin, and Chaplin had recalled the time he had introduced Winston Churchill to the great Sid Perelman, and I had replied that it reminded me somewhat of the time I had been honoured to present dear Edith Evans to The Queen Mother over a breakfast with Larry Olivier, and Mikhail listened intently, in rapt silence, while I entertained him with a rich variety of facial expressions and impersonations before replying — and I think I have now mastered his accent — "Vot a great pleasure zis is to meet yooo, Meester Ustinov, hev yooo met my vife Raisa?" To which I replied that this sterling introduction reminded me of the time that I was in the White House at a small dinner party including the lovely Maggie Smith and Eleanor Roosevelt, and Frank Sinatra, leaning across to my old chum Jackson Pollock, had said, in that very American voice of his: "Wayle, Meester Pollock, howw doooo yoo dooo?" and of course we all roared with laughter.

What, people are always asking me, I don't know why me in particular, but it is a question they often ask, is my definition of charm? I always like to reply with a line from one of my less well-known plays, *Romanoff and Juliet* (1961), which Mr P. Smith in the Letters column of the *Surrey Advertiser* was good enough to describe as "an enjoyable night out for the family, and why not take in a meal beforehand at the new theatre restaurant, convenient and what's more delicious." "Charm", says Romanoff, "is a five-letter word beginning with 'C' and ending with 'M'!" As you would suspect, this line, which I sometimes deliver with a strong Serbo-Croat accent, can be relied upon to draw roars of laughter, but, I would suggest, it contains a more profound truth which mankind will overlook at its peril.

My particular sensibility takes refuge in laughter as others may take refuge in tears, in murder, or in suicide. I am burdened with the ability to make others laugh, yet underneath my charming exterior there lies a decent, sensitive (sometimes painfully so) soul who cares for humanity rather too much for his own good and speaks twelve languages fluently as well as having appeared in over thirty-five feature films. As Zsa Zsa Gabor once said to me in her strong Hungarian accent: "Peeeder, yoooo hev zooooo metch *telent*. Ze whole verld is in lerf viz yooo. End Peeder, yoooo are zooo *profownt*." Yet what is profundity but a convoluted way of expressing the obvious? My own original aphorisms, if one can call them that, are leavened with humour yet contain, I am told, deep oceans of wisdom. Might I offer you one or two from my forthcoming book, *Pardon My Profundity: The Wit and Wisdom of Peter Ustinov*?

"Too great a preponderance of chefs in the *cuisine* can seriously impair the good flavour of any broth therein created" (1967).

"Those who would embark upon a journey to destinations unknown by means of a single, protracted leap would be well advised to observe the area wherein they propose to land before first casting loose from *terra firma*" (1958).

"It is, when all is said and done, an amusing, not to say comical, and indubitably ancient world upon which we humans seek to live, breathe and make merry" (1981).

Until next time, thank you for your kind applause.

MICK JAGGER

Okay, right. Yeah-hay! Let's get this show on the road, shall we? Whoooh! Action! The whole thing about this writing thing is that it's a totally different thing from the performing thing, right? I mean, the whole point of writing is that you want to convey your whole thing to the audience through words but you can't go na na na na na na na na and make a song outtavit, can you? So what are you left with? W-O-R-D-S. Words. Like hundreds of butterflies, only less sort of fluttery and you see more of them about than you do butterflies.

I'm just a kid in a rock 'n' roll band and I don't mind telling you I'm getting totally pissed off with the way they keep saying I'm too old. They've been saying that for the past twenny-five years. If it wasn't true twenny-five years ago, why should it be any more true now?

Tell you one thing. You can stay a rock 'n' roll kid forever just so long as you still get turned on by what's happening streetwise. No one can tell me I'm not wise to what's happening in our street. Cheyne Walk, Chelsea is just five miles from the East End of London

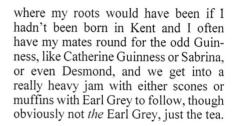

where my roots would have been if I hadn't been born in Kent and I often have my mates round for the odd Guinness, like Catherine Guinness or Sabrina, or even Desmond, and we get into a really heavy jam with either scones or muffins with Earl Grey to follow, though obviously not *the* Earl Grey, just the tea.

Most far-out place I've ever been in all my travels round this crazy world? The place with the most beautiful people and the most spaced-out scenery? To my mind that place is definitely oh christ what's it called, nyaah, 's gone.

I'm still totally into the Blues, even more so since that John Major's become their boss, 'cos I think ninety per cent tax, blah blah blah, is totally pernicious but totally. For instance, from the royalties of *Street Fightin' Man* I couldn't even get enough to finish off the jacuzzi in the South of France, and I had to move to Jamaica for three months to avoid paying the totally pernicious tax on the *Feed the Poor Kids, Mr Rich Fucker* from the *Down 'n' Out in Harlem* protest album.

The Sixties. Great times that still live in the memory. I'll never forget the day f'rinstance when Keith — or Bill, it was either Keith or Bill, it certainly wasn't the other one, thingy — came up to me in the Savoy, it must have been, or Claridges, yeah, that's right, the Connaught, and he looked me in the face and he said, "John," he said, and I said, "Mick, actually," and he said, "Yeah, thas right, Mick," he said, "Mick, I wanna tell you one thing, man," and I said, "What's that, Brian or whoever," and he said something I'll never forget to the day that I die. Actually, I can't remember absolutely what he said now that I think about it, but it stuck in my mind for one helluva long time and I think it's nice to remind ourselves of that kind of thing now that the guy's dead, that's if he *is* dead, of course.

Me and Keith's songs have progressed a long way since the Sixties. I mean, compare this line from the Sixties:

"I can't get no
Na na na na na
Can't get no
Na na na na na
Sa-tis
Fac-shun"

to this far more complex line from the Seventies:

"It's only rock 'n' roll
But I like it
Like it
Yes I do
Yes I like it
I like it."

Right up to where we are right now in the Eighties with infinitely and I mean infinitely more politically and emotionally *aware* lines like:

"I can't get no
Rock 'n' Roll
But I try and I try
To like it
Like it
'Specially in places like El Salvador
Na na na na na."

So let's hear no more of that the-Stones-aren't-goin'-nowhere-they're-stuck-in-the-Sixties scene hassle rap we've been gettin' recently 'cos it's draggin' me and the other freaks down, okay man? 'Nuff said. Rock on.

Remember Brian Jones (1943ish-1960something)? RIP. Beautiful guy. Dear friend. As I said at Hyde Park, Brian was a butterfly whose wings were too light to lift heavy machinery or even a bongo so I had to tell him to piss off. Peace, peace, as the poet Shirley put it, he is not dead, he dusts both sheep.

I'm not particularly into the money thing but over the years I've accrued considerable earnings from capital gained as a result of shrewd long-term investment by experienced advisers, but as I say I'm not the kinda guy who's gonna get looned out on material possessions blah blah blah. I still keep in touch with my roots and my heart's still with — yeaahhh! — rock 'n' roll, as I was tellin' Princess Margaret — d'y'know her? — only last night, or was it the night before? I forget. She seemed pretty shagged off with the whole Royalty rap and the total shaking hands thing, and I was telling her that there might be a place for her with a tambourine on the next tour, kind of Linda McCartney trip. Like I said, Margaret, it would be really cool if you'd join us, but there's a like favour you could do me in return. I mean, as you know, I'm not into the whole aristocracy thing, but I'd like to accept a knighthood not just for myself but on behalf of the whole world of rock 'n' roll, dig it. So if the next time we're playing Wembley you spot just behind Keith a fat chick in a tiara you'll know to start addressing us as Sir Michael and Lady Jerry or whatever, but that obviously needn't apply to close friends, family, and financial associates, etc. Rock 'n' roll! Whoooo! Right ON!!

PRINCESS MICHAEL OF KENT

May I first say how delighted I am that my PR representative — who, incidentally, has asked me to make it known that he also handles many other leading entertainers, such as Bobby Davro, the Roly-Polys, Martyn Lewis, Christopher Biggins, Freddie "Parrot Face" Davis and my sister, Mrs Angie Best — has arranged with the editor and staff of this "humorous" magazine that I should contribute to their prestigious diary as part of my career relaunch. Might I just add that, as from early May, I will be available, with or without my husband, Prince Michael of Kent, who is, as you know, President of the British Bobsleigh Federation, for all types of entertainment and celebration, ranging from cookery demonstrations and plaza openings through to dinner-dances and celebrity panel-games. Mr Jim Bowen of television's popular *Bullseye* programme has already shown a keen interest in having me appear in his excellent show's "celebrity guest" slot, and Mr Des O'Connor, an old friend of the family from way back, seems sure that he can find a space for me on his new series, probably to close duetting with him on "Edelweiss", that charming song from my fatherland from my hit musical *The Sound of Music*. You may remember that I played Maria Von Trapp in the highly successful film version.

For obvious reasons which we needn't go into, she has received virtually no publicity, but there has, in the last few years, been a new member of The Royal Family whom avid watchers might have observed from time to time. She is a Miss Sarah Ferguson, the daughter of a self-confessed ticket-tout. Good for her, and I for one wish her every success, but am I alone in worrying that she is not quite — how shall I put it? — top drawer?. It is most important in these trying times that those of us in the vanguard of The Royal Family take extra pains to guard the dignity and awe in which we are held by "the common folk". This young lady, or person, for all her considerable talents (she is, I am told, quite gifted at "pulling faces") is perhaps in danger of letting the side down. Let us please, please, please preserve something of our traditional mystique. This was a point I was putting to Gloria Hunniford and top comedian Jim "Nick-Nick" Davidson over a delicious complimentary meal at Stringfellow's hosted by Nigel Dempster only last week. Perhaps for her own sake Fleet Street editors might consider the value of a "news blackout" on Miss Ferguson, poor love, for a short period of, say, ten years? I am perfectly prepared to take over the burden of her duties (price list available on request).

Many of you will have wondered these past few years exactly what I have been "up to", as you say in this country. After a chaotic year in 1986, I was given the most marvellous surprise holiday — a complete rest in an upper tower of delightful Glamis Castle, where I was fed regularly and unstrapped under supervision for an hour every second Tuesday. During this time, I was forced to keep a "low profile", as the ceiling was only 4ft 6ins, and spiked. Following a very pleasant couple of months spent amidst these historic surroundings, I was happy to sign a declaration of my wish to spend more time with my family for the next five years. But now it is 1991 at last, and I know that my return to public life will give a lot of pleasure to a lot of people — not least to my accountant!

In the meantime, I have been working hard, very hard. I have written no less than three books. Two of them are novels — *David Kopperfield*, a long tale set in Victorian times, and *Nurse Zhivago*, a panoramic novel set amidst the turmoil of the Russian Revolution. The third, an exciting new departure for me, is a children's book which I have called *Pudgie the Little Helicopter*, and the proceeds of which will be going to one of my favourite charities, "The British Bobsleigh Federation (Widows Trust)". Now my Royal duties are as onerous as ever; only last week I journeyed to Aberdeen to take part in a mud-wrestling competition (£325 and all expenses paid) and the week before I recorded an episode of *Blankety Blank* as part of an all-star line-up including the hilarious John Inman, Radio One's Dave Lee Travis and pocket-sized chanteuse Lynsey de Paul. I hope that this will stem some of the criticism in various newspapers that we in The Royal Family have not been doing our bit during the recent conflict.

Thank goodness the rumour-mongers have ceased their idle tittle-tattle about myself and my husband, who, on his marriage to me, became Prince Michael of Kent. He is now shaping up to be a very useful member of our Family, a thoroughly worthy escort to his wife and something of a character in his own right, with a beard of his own, quite a few conversations to hand, and so on.

As a couple, I think that the nation will join with me in agreeing that we are now ideally placed to "take over the reins" should anything untoward

happen to that branch of the family occupying the throne at present. To this end, I have flown over my mother, Mrs Eileen Skunk (née Countess Rogala-Kozacorawski) of the upmarket high class *haute couture* boutique "Odds 'n' Sods" of Sydney, Australia, for an intensive training course in acting the role of Queen Mum. After just two weeks, she is already able to hold a knife and fork, and within a month her tutor confidently expects her to be able to place her gum behind her right ear without first saying, "Time to give the old phlegm a bit of a breather." By early May, she will be out of her dungarees and into some specially-purchased crinolines, and come June she will have learnt to walk in shoes. This means that, just so long as the present occupant does not die before July, we will be ideally situated to substitute a brand new Queen Mother into place within minutes of the full state funeral. With HRH Queen Eileen the Queen Mother in position, the present Queen will find herself in the invidious position of failing to be the true daughter of the new Queen Mother. I have the very greatest respect for her integrity and I know that the country can count on her to accede quietly and responsibly with the barest minimum of fuss in favour of Queen Marie-Christine. And I am delighted to say that my husband has kindly agreed to act as consort until a more suitable replacement can be found. God Bless You All.

ANTHONY BURGESS

Breakfast, literally speaking the fasting of one's breaks or, from the early Nordic "Brr — eat fast", as the Vikings would say when the weather was chilly, is not only one of the few words in the Anglo-Saxon tongue to possess an "ak" immediately followed by a "fa" at its epicentre (another such word being "akfa", a probable mis-spelling of "aqua", meaning the opposite of no-water) but it is also my preferred meal.

The British Establishment — largely and probably unknowingly transvestitic and certainly increasingly cannibalistic — has never understood breakfast. They go for slices of pig and the encaged remains of an unfertilised embryonic bird to set them on their feet. Coming from a long line of Lancashire Roman Catholics, I stick to porridge, or, rather, it sticks to me. Porridge, or, etymologically speaking, "pour-ridge", is rightly ladled in a pouring motion over all the ridges of one's visage or face, and this tradition I maintain each morning. Porridge poured everywhere is good for the brain and for the skin, and its multi-lumpitextuosity accounts for the splendour of my hairstyle, which retains some oats first poured in the year of our Lord 1935.

I have always found the look and smell of a bottle of Heinz tomato ketchup powerfully erotic, in that noble word's original sense of "tasting slightly of tomatoes". In the contemporary sense of the word, it is not erotic at all, or at any rate not nearly as erotic as a can of tinned peaches in heavy syrup, one of which I remember taking to the opera and courting successfully in the spring of '48, only to be turned down when it came to bed because it had become suspicious of my infatuation with a beautifully ripe pineapple. All full-blooded Englishmen, particularly those of Irish descent, have found sexual desire within their loins for the suppurating convexities and soft, skeiny protuberances of the fruit (originally "froo-it", owing to the fact that, if it had an unrelenting central core, it was hard to bite froo it), and this explains why the Establishment has never allowed a law to be placed on the statute books forbidding full intercourse with any type of fruit.

The English, by which I mean to say those who live in England, have always made the mistake of wearing wellington boots on their feet when it is wet. I have a sturdy pair of wellington boots myself, but I wear them on my head, never on my feet, and then only when it is sunny. In my 43rd novella, *The Wellington Boot Wearer*, I portrayed a Lancastrian working-class Catholic battling with the inherent forces of evil who takes to wearing wellington boots, but ill-advisedly not on his/her (the man is a trans-sexual) head but on the feet. The book closes with his death at the hands, or rather mouth, of an escaped lion, a symbol of the deity, perhaps, who has been fed for over twenty years solely on wellington boots. I wrote the novel with the intention of suggesting that if the unnamed hero had followed my advice to wear his wellingtons on his head, and then only when sunny, he might still be alive, for it was rainy when the lion escaped. But did they listen? On my frequent visits back to this beleaguered Isle, I am amazed by the continued wearing of wellingtons on feet, despite my prophetic warning. But then the English have never understood serious fiction, sending those of us who are its foremost practitioners into exile, forcing us to write for the *Daily Mail*, denying us knighthoods, turning our creations into musicals.

People say that my failing is that I cannot concentrate — interesting word, spelt backwards emerging as "etartnecnoc", a meaningless jumble of letters — but this is intolerable and untrue. They also say that I am a master of the *non sequitur*, leaping from one subject to another when they do not follow. For the past year I have not been following the patchy progress of my neighbour Graham Greene, a very undistinguished writer and a grumpy old bat, with whom my argument escalates, though the escalator, or, in French, *escalateur*, goes down as well as up, echoing, in a quasi-mysto-mechanical way, the descent and subsequent ascension of Lord Jesus Christ, who was, of course, not a Lord at all, as the Anglo-Saxons, being riddled with snobbery, like to think, but a carpenter, in fact I believe in this country there is a sporting commentator called Harry or Harold Carpenter, though whether he has ridden on a moving staircase or not we have no way of knowing. Where was I? Ah, yes: *concentration*. There is a concentrated orange juice — Ki-Ora, now there's a funny word, and Bivouac, there's another — but when we talk of concentration we mean something more than orange juice, moving staircases, sporting commentators, Graham Greene, or even Jesus Christ, but now I've lost my thread, which is, incidentally, an anagram of "dearth".

I make frequent appearances on what in this country is known as the

★ STAR THOUGHTS ★

EDWARD DE BONO

Nothing can happen until something happens. Something happening cannot be nothing. But when something happens, nothing cannot happen. The happening is nothing if not something, yet nothing is happening. Or something.

You are wrong, I am right. I am right you are wrong. You are Ron, I am Reg. But who is he?

television, often to talk about my latest opera, novel, cookery book, hymnal or work of literary criticism. I have recently extended my range so that I am now available for cabaret turns, golf club dances, and bar mitzvahs, singing a selection from *Showboat*, reciting the seven French nouns whose plurals end in "oux", demonstrating New Developments in the Handjive, presenting a course of lectures on Michel de Montaigne or all at the same time. In the summer, I will be touring the country in the company of my barber and a leading manufacturer of porridge oats, and at the end of each show the audience will be invited up onto the stage to taste my hair while I read extracts from my new six-hundred-page *magnum opus*, which details the tribulations of a homosexual Cardinal in Singapore confronted by a triumvirate of Yahweh, an Unnamed Force and Destiny, as he performs his ablutions upon the lavatory, though it is finally established that they have called at the wrong address. It is, in its oblique way, a chronicle of our century. I look forward to seeing you all there.

CLIVE JAMES

People have been kind enough to call me sharp. To be blunt, I am sharp. It was probably Rilke who first taught me that if ever a man is to be sharp, he needs also to be blunt. This was a revelation to me, and partly because I already knew it. The sharp man must make pointed statements in rounded prose, remaining careful that the points emerge from his heart, and not from his head, or they will come out flat. Voltaire, too, taught me to square my feelings with my thoughts, particularly when talking among my circle.

If I am a master of the easy paradox, it is essentially because no paradox is easy to master. My prose style is the style of a pro (se). The clever effect is achieved by reversing the first half of a sentence so that the reversal achieves an effect of cleverness. This has gained me an international reputation for being smart, though I am not one to smart at the international reputation I have gained.

Ronald Reagan is a man who walks tall, and, walking tall, the free world looks up to him. Looking up to him, the free world walks tall, walks as tall as Ronald Reagan. Ronald Reagan may walk tall, but he also talks walls. The Berlin wall was also a Burly Wall when Ronald Reagan came to the Presidency of the United States of America, but by the time he left office it was a Hurly-Burly wall, not a tall wall at all but a short wall which had just had a shortfall. Now people could step over it, in a way that they could never step over Ronald Reagan.

Ronald Reagan met me a few weeks back, and he seemed pleased to shake my hand. My hand, in turn, seemed pleased to shake his. But there was nothing shaky about the way he addressed himself to my probing questions, and sure enough my probing questions were asked at his address. Even Shakespeare might have felt a little "Shaky" on meeting Clive James, but not Ronald.

If I am known to all, and there is no reason other than my worldwide popularity to believe that I am, it is as a fearless and incisive champion for truth. Too thin on top to be compared to Einstein with complete accuracy, I am nevertheless humble enough to admit to having been born with a dazzling armoury of wit and an impressive command of the language. Small wonder, then, that the ex-President was ex-pressing himself a little dented by my presence in his ex-tremely im-Pressive den.

My questions were carefully judged to be hard-hitting without hitting hard, forceful without being full of force. In this manner, Reagan ended up getting more out of me than many a more aggressive interviewer. Of course, many of the most interesting answers were never screened. For instance, when Reagan said, "Did you come far?", I replied with a brief but mercilessly funny resumé of my biography. I began with an anecdote concerning the condition of my donger after I had plonked it once too often in the sheep-dip. I then talked him through the lighter side of the notably incautious acne I experienced throughout a prolonged adolescence. I spoke movingly of the moment as a wide-eyed and gifted Cambridge undergraduate when I first realised that I was not only wide-eyed but gifted. I spoke as briefly as humility would allow of my television reviews from the early '70s, with extracts from my classic "Game for a Laugh? Game for a Bath, More Like!" review (since reprinted in many anthologies). And I wound up by telling the great man that I was now proud to dine out on a regular basis with the Duke and Duchess of York. "So, yes, Mr President," I concluded, "I think you could indeed say I've come far!!" And you know, under that gently sleeping exterior, I think I detected a chuckle.

My first question to Ronald Reagan — "You were undoubtedly the best-loved President in the history of your country" — lacked for nothing save, perhaps, a question mark. My second question — "Would you mind awfully, Mr President, if I were to declare that you were a hero not only to countless millions of your fellow countrymen but also to me personally?" — was intended to soften him up for the third question — "You are undoubtedly an excellent horseman. What is it about horse-riding that you find so appealing?" This one took him aback a bit. I could tell that he hadn't been expecting anything quite so piercing. But the old charmer forgave me afterwards with another warm handshake. "Pleasure to meet you, Mr-er-er-" he said, in a revealing aside, too overcome with joy of our meeting to be able to splutter out my name.

I am sometimes fiercely criticised for being able to write as brilliantly about the great French poet Eugenio Montale or the revolutionary Italian composer Wittgenstein as about TV commercials for Maxwell House Instant Coffee. Solemnity, I am well aware, is not my best vein. Lacking all pomposity, it is pomposity that I find myself most lacking. Low subjects or high, I find myself saying "Hi" to subjects others see as low. And to subjects that are high I trust I have learnt the humility to say "Lo!"

If my reading of Dietrich Bonhoeffer — much of it in the original Russian — has taught me anything, it is that Instant Coffee granules and Eugenio Montale differ only in the things that make them unalike: it is in their similarities that one finds them much the same. You may not be able to spoon Montale into a cup and stir him up without making an old man very cross, but still you may find yourself saying "ah!" and asking for more upon sipping his dark brown prose.

The youth who once hoped for royalties is now the man who dines with royalty. The student who once read *Nietzsche* in sobriety is now the guy who has found his *niche* in society. Born to the upper crust, Princess Margaret now counts it a privilege to be borne to eat pastry crust with myself. The bloke from the outback who satire weaned is now the sophisticated *litterateur* whose attire gleams. These and other brilliant, caustic aphorisms have earned me my place at life's top table, but I know that human nature is various, and I have never been pleased enough about my own nature to feel contemptuous about anybody else's. I therefore take pride in offering a helping heel to those still struggling, and, as for those few still above, I do my best to help them cross their 'T's and lick their 'R's.

NIGEL KENNEDY

Dadaladadaladadaladadaladadaladadalala lumpumdompompPOM! Recognise it? *Hocus Pocus* by Focus, one band that can really kick ass in my book. Just 'cos I'm a so-called prominent classical musician — meaning, if you'll pardon my French, shit-hot on the fiddle — people expect me to only get off on Ludwig and Wolfy and all them other dead blokes. Sure, I dig them, who doesn't, but who's to say I can't get my rocks off on some of the really modern up-to-date real groovy and outasight stuff too? Blimey, as I'm scribbling this shit down I'm filling my lugholes with a mega-ace disc that's as modern as they make 'em, and it's really blowing my mind — *In The Court Of The Crimson King* by King Crimson. Phew! Mega-brill! My current playlist also includes *Honky Tonk Women* by the Rolling Stones, *Nursery Crymes* by Genesis, Mike Oldfield's brilliant new follow-up album, *Hergest Ridge* and the mega-vibey new one by Guys and Dolls. Okay, so I make the odd shekel gigging with the sounds of yesteryear — but that doesn't mean my head isn't really into the sounds of today, man!

Koncerning The Klassix (1): Ludwig Van Beethoven was one helluva bloke who lived really years ago and died really years ago too but whose music lives on. Ludwig had mega-wild hair, sproutin' out like an 'edge'og, but no one told *him* where to get off, no one told *him* to put a comb thru' it. So why do they persecute *me* just cos I wanna be a little bit

mega-hip? Sometimes I think you have to be dead before you're really appreciated, know what I mean? Cor, I could *murder* a curry right now.

(One monster curry later, folks!) BURP! One helluva mega madras that — best open all windows!! Down to biz. As you probably know, I'm an Aston Villa nutcase. What I love about the game is when you're on those terraces you merge with the rest of the crowd, who are just completely normal blokes, and you feel this great sense of oneness. You're no longer the world-famous mega-superstar Nigel Kennedy who can command six-figure sums and is admired by millions of fans and has been on *This Is Your Life* with Michael Aspel, you're no longer the young bloke who singlehandedly brought the Klassix to a universal audience, you're no longer the idol of mega-billions of people who queue overnight for your Viv gigs, you're no longer the bloke who lives dangerously by breaking moulds, no, you're just one of a large group of supporters all rooting for the Villa. That literally amazing sense of losing your own identity in the crowd for a common purpose is just — well, literally amazing. And it gives all the normal blokes in the crowd a monster buzz, too, to realise that Nigel Kennedy is there shoutin' and stompin' his support along with the rest of 'em, so I make a point of dressin' up in me fancy shoes and me shorts and me punk hairstyle and carryin' me Strad into the front seat of the directors' box so they can all see that I'm out there with 'em, leadin' the way, and I think they appreciate the fact that I'm just as mega-normal as them.

*K*oncerning the Klassix (2): Johann Sebastian Bach was another shit-hot musician who got messed about from time to time so in the end he just buckled down to a bourgeois lifestyle after all those negative vibes. I frankly don't know whether he supported Aston Villa or not, or even whether the Villa was around at that time, but if he did he kept his Villa scarf pretty much to himself, you never see it in photos of the bloke. I like to think I've struck a blow for the cat Johann by not being afraid to wear my Aston Villa scarf when performing on stage in monster halls. It's what he'd like to have done, but what society would never let him do, poor geezer, and now he's dead, shame really. Cor, could I do with a six-pack of Stella.

*F*rankly, I've always been a bit of a rebel, get the vibe? I don't like to swallow too much bullshit and I like to do my own thing. Is that a crime? By the way I've been persecuted by the Establishment, you might be forgiven for thinking it was. Talk about megahassles. Blimey. I was never able to wrap my head around bullshit, even as a child, and I was always, like, cocking a thingy at authority and that made them really pissed off. When I was twelve and still at school, I would sometimes take my milk and biscuits when it was time for elevenses and then secretly not drink all my milk and only eat, say, one biscuit. Then when I was a bit older — thirteen or fourteen — and I was expected to conform to the bourgeois standards of the so-called classical establishment I would regularly do my own thing by making clucking noises with my tongue when no one was around. By fifteen, I was discarding all the green Opal Fruits from the Opal Fruits packet just because I didn't fancy them and I saw no reason why I should be forced to eat them, by sixteen, I was wearing jeans in my free-time, and by seventeen I had bought my first album by The New Seekers, containing the mega-brill and far-out *Beg, Steal or Borrow* number which I really dug. I guess I've always been one of life's outsiders, a natural eccentric or a bit of a nutter, whichever way you wanna look at it. Is that a crime?

*S*ome stuffy buggers might not think it's cool, but I break moulds in my sleep. There's a heap of negative tosh written knocking me by blokes who know sod all about music: bullshit, you might call it, and I've never had much patience with that stuff. I'll go on breaking moulds even if they carry on trying to gag me, and that's because, as I've said, I'm a rebel. You don't deliberately wear one sock inside-out for a bet when you are seventeen and then start conforming for the men in grey when you hit thirty-four, no way. When I'm not breaking moulds, I'm knockin' down barriers. I share with my elocution tutor, the mega-brill David Essex, a genuine love of *Bohemian Rhapsody* by Queen, so I'm now planning to record my version of it, adding a backing track by Claude Debussy so as to rope more fans into digging it. Meanwhile, my old mate Paul Gascoigne, better known to one and all as Gazza, has agreed to recite *The Love Song of J. Alfred Prufrock* over the top, so as to break down the snobby barriers that exist between that groovebag T.S. Eliot and Association Football. Some la-di-da critics might tell you that the project says somethin' about the state of my head, but to me the whole thing should be really gear! Until next time, keep on truckin' guys 'n' gals!

HRH PRINCE PHILIP

Seventieth b'day party last week. Why on *earth* does everyone wrap their bloody presents in that ghastly coloured paper? Takes up valuable time, muck everywhere, wastes money we can ill afford. And what's that infernal sticky stuff called? Sellotape. Sello-bloody-tape. What's the *point* of it? Could some-one please tell me? Eh? That's what I'd like to know. Eh? Makes whatever you're being fobbed off with — socks, hand-kerchiefs and other such nonsense — harder to unpack as well as buggering up the coloured paper so that it can't be reused.

Fat lot of good some of my "presents" were. Silk socks from the sister-in-law. "Do I *look* like a silk socks man? Do I? Do I? Eh?" I said, by way of thank you. Some characters can get terribly testy if you don't say your thank yous in the traditional soppy manner. I have a feel-ing I ruffled Margaret's feathers because she stormed out in the most goddawful huff. "Bloody hell," I said, "Operation Smooth-Over into action once again."

Stormed out after Margaret. Found her sulking in the sherry cupboard, straw already in mouth. "C'mon, old girl, chins up, wipe those tears away", I said, sympatheti-cally. "I did the damn thank yous didn't I? I love the silk socks, love 'em." I could see she was struggling to

muster a smile. "It's just that I'm not one of your damn nancy-boy cocktail guests. Who d'you think I am? Sir Roy Bloody Strong?" In my experience, such quips can be guaranteed to "smooth things over". But much to my surprise, Margaret turned on the old waterworks again, sobbing all over the shop. Happy Birthday? Happy Birthday my arse.

The ordinary bloke — or blokes! — in the street or in the place of work is always delighted to see one. A bit of a quip and a decent backslap from myself does much to boost our export drive. Humour's a great bond, I find, and I often kick off an introduction with Joe Bloggs with a humorous remark. Before getting down to brass tacks with the How-long-have-you-worked-heres and the What-exactly-do-you-dos, I like to say something a bit more personal along the lines of:

a) "Aren't you too fat for a job like this?!"

b) "Is that bloody awful pong com-ing from you?!"

c) "Speaka da Inglesi?!"

or, if the bloke needs to be "drawn out" a bit:

d) "I'd guess you were working class. Do you enjoy it? Conversation pretty limited, I'd imagine, but camaraderie excellent, eh? Good show. Keep whis-tling."

Needless to say, they love it, often letting out a great cheer as one departs.

Had Mother Teresa of Calcutta to dinner last week. Dead loss. Pecked at her food. Pooh-poohed a beer. Quiet as a nun. Her conversation wasn't going great guns: not a thing to say on carriage-driving, for instance, or grouse for that matter, and when I drew the talk round to topics of more general interest it emerged that she didn't have much to say about catamarans either. Heavy-going to say the least, so I finally plucked some of my tried and tested "puns" out of the air to set her at her ease.

"For this joke to work," I began, "you have to imagine that there's a fellow called Cal. Okay? Eh? Make myself clear? Eh? Eh? Right. This chap Cal has a young lady friend who we'll just call 'Her', are you still with me? One day, Cal — you remember Cal, of course, from the beginning of the joke? You're looking pretty blank. Sometimes I don't know why I bother, I really don't. We don't *have* to give these dinner-parties, you know. We could just stay at home watching the bloody telly like everyone else. Anyway, so Cal is playing with a knife one day and — and here comes the punch-line — by mistake 'CAL CUT HER'. Do you see? 'CAL-CUT-'ER — CALCUTTA'. Eh? Eh? Oh, bloody hell. Why bother? Pass the veg then, sharpish, sharpish".

O n a less lighthearted note, I have, over the course of a busy life, run up a fair number of speeches. These have been published in such books as *Preserving Birdlife: A Future for Bloodsports* (1972), *Towards A Shipshape World: Lectures on Moral Philosophy* (1981), and *Mind Your Backs: Essays on Overpopulation* (1988). But these thoughts of mine don't just come from nowhere, you know. If that's what you thought, you're even more of an imbecile than I thought. Far from it: my philosophy has emerged after many hours talking to and — almost as important — *listening* to some of the greatest philosophists of our time. David Attenborough, Sir Harry Secombe, Blashford-Snell, Lord Tony Pandy. The lot. Mind you, some of the so-called "professionals" are a dead loss. No practical ability. The other day, I snatched a bite to eat with Isaiah Berlin, the renowned philosophist. "Right," I said, "you're the great philosophist. You've tackled questions of good and bad. Let's bash a few ideas around the court. *Shorts*, for instance. Good or bad? Eh? Eh? Good or bad? Speak up! Eh?"

The old fellow obviously didn't have the foggiest. "Shorts?" he replied. "I'm sorry, what do you mean by the term 'Shorts'?"

"For crying out loud!" I said. "Shorts! Little trousers, cut off above the knee. Worn with long socks. Let the air in. *Shorts!* Do you believe in 'em, yea or nay? Good or bad? Come on! Come on!"

No idea. Face a blank. The simplest question, and not a sausage. Here's a chap who's probably prepared to prognosticate on God and Truth and Life and so on, yet he can't even make up his mind on shorts!!

Personally, I'm all for them, particularly when barbecuing. But then I'm no "intellectual" — I'm delighted to say!

S ick to death department. I'm sick to death of professional whingers living on state handouts and thinking that they have earned the god-given right to tell ordinary, decent people what's what. More often than not, you'll find that they live very comfortably, thank you, with car, house, colour TV, yacht, etcetera all paid for by the taxpayer, and getting a bit extra from their wives too, if I'm not mistaken. Yet they continue to strut around as if they owned the bloody place (and some of them weren't even born here, though we're not allowed to say that!) effing and blinding in a manner to suggest that Britain owes them a living, and, I daresay, probably inventing new surnames for themselves so as to reap additional benefits. Should this sort of person really have a say in the nation's affairs? Well, should he? Eh? Eh?

PAUL JOHNSON

Once again, Spring, that damnable season, is coming round. This means more hard slog in the garden. Like most sensible people, I hate the sight of flowers, with all their hideous yellows and pinks and oranges. Yet in Spring new flowers appear every day. Any gardener worth his salt will get up specially early, axe in one hand, a sharp pair of secateurs in t'other, and chop off any militant bud as soon as it puts its head above ground.

Needless to say, the left-dominated BBC is in this, as in most other matters, out of tune with the British public. A new season of so-called "gardening" programmes is upon us. These programmes make all the right liberal noises about beautiful blooms, lovely petals and such nonsense, and they are presented by the inevitable array of females, homosexuals and men in boots. But I have yet to see a single "gardening" programme giving the other point of view. Why, for instance, has there been nothing explaining to the average viewer how to take a chainsaw to a rose-bush? The truth of the matter is that the BBC lives in fear of offending the liberal hierarchy which holds its purse-strings, flower-sniffers to a man.

When work is done, man must needs have his rest. I have always been a great believer in fun, and for this reason I ban gramophones, transistor radios, televisions, "videos", toasters or any other type of mechanical contrivance from my home. Our amusements are traditional. They are centred upon the paper-hat, the blindfold, the penny whistle, and the good old-fashioned sing-song. The fun begins with myself as Head of the House being blindfolded by my wife and assorted offspring. They then place a paper-hat upon my head and a penny whistle in my mouth, and for their entertainment I accompany myself on a full solo rendition of the Complete Works of Gilbert and Sullivan. This takes between fourteen and fifteen hours, certainly not longer. They tell me that they sit enraptured throughout. Oddly enough, when I completed the final rousing chorus of *The Pirates of Penzance* at the end of our last Fun Evening, I removed my blindfold to find not a soul there. After doughty detective-work, I located them at a local speakeasy, sipping lurid cocktails and watching *Beadle's About* in the company of black men. Roy Jenkins and the creeping liberalisation of the Sixties still have much to answer for. Before tonight's fun kicks off, I will be locking all doors, barring all windows, and applying good, strong chains to all seats.

What a lot of tosh is whined about Freedom of Speech by the rent-a-protest lobby of Socialist millionaires and their backers! Most ordinary, decent citizens care not a fig for dubious literature espousing subversive, anti-British values, often in a sexually explicit manner. Fashionable Hampstead authors might feel that they have some form of god-given right to parade their left-wing consciences upon the bookshelves of our great cities, but this argument, like its filthy-necked proponents, simply will not wash. Most intelligent people are content to read nothing but my own works, and they have no wish to be dictated to by the likes of Salman Rushdie and the Trendy Left. Yet the vast majority of my own works are now remaindered or unread. Is it not time for the Government to take a firm stand?

Any writer worth his salt should be able to turn his hand to the light-hearted occasional essay. I have a sturdy, thoroughly British sense of humour. I laughed on no less than eight different occasions last year, five of them at remarks I myself had made, and I always welcome the opportunity to amuse and enlighten others. My weekend pieces for the *Daily Telegraph* — "In Praise of the Bicycle Clip", "The Pleasures of Stinging-Nettles", "Stamping on Small, Furry Animals" — were notable for their winning combination of sound advice and jocular asides, and I continue to receive up to five hundred letters a week — many of them written by myself — from grateful readers.

I fear that no such sense of humour resides on the Left. I cannot see Mr Harold Pinter or his ilk chuckling at, say, the robust good humour of Mr Mike Gatting, even though his courage in defying the killjoys of the totalitarian Left is an inspiration to many. This explains the poverty of so much so-called comedy on the BBC. Unashamedly left-wing productions like *Dad's Army* and *Terry and June*, with their incessant sniping at institutions forged by traditional values, such as the Armed Forces and the family, have done much to destroy our image abroad. The cynical destruction of all we hold dear is no substitute for a sense of humour.

Leftish scare-stories are rife. The current systematic whispering campaign against "Bovine Spongiform" is only the latest in a long line. I have long found that Bovine Spongiform is a tremendous asset to any writer worth his salt. If it were not, I would be the first to know, as editors employ me for my clear-thinking and sound commonsense. Only this morning, the phone rang, and, as I danced this way and that in circular motions en route to answer it, I felt my head butt against the wall and my leg kick robustly through a door, and I thought to myself, "Cock-a-doodle-doo". Picking up the receiver, I found that, with the application of a decent bit of sticky tape, it could be made to resemble a perfectly good moustache, which I am wearing as I write. Incidentally, I have long argued that typing with one's "plonker" saves one's fists for banging the table and hurling things, and all my articles are written in this way. So let us hear no more from those politically-motivated fanatics who would wish to manipulate our minds against this fine, thoroughly British, disease.

★ STAR THOUGHTS ★
W. F. DEEDES

Not every fad catches on, thank goodness. "Jeans", for instance. I remember in the late '50s a very senior member of the Government taking me to one side and saying that these brittle cotton trousers were soon to be all the rage. Yet one never heard of them again. And many moons ago, we were told by the so-called "experts" that the 78 gramophone record had had its day, and that it was soon to be replaced by something newer and better. But nothing whatsoever came along to replace it, and my own collection of 78 gramophone records is still affording me much pleasure.

But last weekend I had my first taste of a new fad that seems to me to be in with a chance of catching on. I was offered a "Potato Crisp" — a wafer-thin effort, deep-fried until golden then sprinkled with a little salt and placed in a plastic bag. The manufacturers of these comestibles tell me they have hopes for their survival as a cocktail "snack". The spirit of enterprise lives on. Full marks all round.

JOHN MORTIMER

"Tell me," I said, wiping the last dribs and drabs of a perfectly acceptable leg of lamb from my chin before reaching over for the pudding menu. "Do you believe in God?"

I was interviewing the Deputy Leader of the Labour Party, Mr Roy Hattersley, for a major profile. I was fascinated to hear what his reply would be.

"One Crème Brûlée for me. No, better make that two — never very filling, I find." The waitress had arrived. Having placed his order, Mr Hattersley returned his attention to the problem in hand. "Sorry, John," he said. "I forgot the question. Do I believe in... "

"Steam pud, with extra treacle and perhaps a spot of double cream, terribly kind." It was now my turn to place my order. I had toyed with a Fudge Sundae, but had eventually plumped for the Steam Pud, that fine old pre-Thatcher, thoroughly English dish. Once again, I resumed my conversation with the Deputy Leader of the Labour Party and Shadow Home Secretary. "Sorry, Roy," I said. "You were saying?"

"You asked if I believed in something-or-other, but I didn't quite catch it," said Roy, dislodging a stray smidgin

of smoked salmon from his hind teeth with the deft movement of a toothpick.

"Do you think we could manage a *Beaumes de Venise*? Could be just the ticket," I replied.

"A most agreeable suggestion, which I am unafraid to endorse wholeheartedly," chuckled Roy.

"Now, where were we?" I asked, resuming our interview.

"Which of you's the Steam Pud?" said the waitress.

"Rather!" I said.

"And you're the Crème Brûlée," said the waitress.

"That looks jolly good," enthused Roy.

After *Beaumes de Venise*, a good cup of strong coffee and a plate or two of *petits fours*, I asked Roy Hattersley a question that always fascinates me. "Do you believe in God?" I said.

"Your car has arrived, Mr Mortimer." It was Lorenzo, to tell me that my car had arrived. Bidding farewell to the Deputy Leader of the Opposition, I departed for home, where I would get my excellent secretary to write up my profile of this most intriguing of politicians, a politician who, it seems, has not yet quite made up his mind about God, one way or t'other.

Things I hate about Britain: the dreadfully divisive class system; the immense vulgarity of the *nouveau-riche*; the absurd nationalism and petty xenophobia of our leadership; the awful American rubbish we allow onto our television screens; a general complacency.

Thatcher's Britain is at long last in its death throes, thanks in no small part to the think-tank of anti-Thatcherite artists and intellectuals who would meet in "safe houses" in the Campden Hill Square area. I was privileged to be a member of this brave *samizdat* organisation, rising to the position of Catering Manager shortly before its dissolution.

Of course, we were subjected to abuse, sneers and vilification by the Thatcherite press, who sensed that, where we led, the "ordinary bloke in the street" would follow. And so he did, as the polls conclusively prove. I now find that, wherever I go, I receive messages of appreciation from all the rag-and-bone men, chimney sweeps and shoe-shine boys who serve me. "Good on yer, sir!" they say, and tears come into their eyes as they brush-brush-brush my sturdy brogues. "You, like, showed 'er what's what. You're a gent, m'lord, and Gor Bless Yer, sir." I love the ordinary people of the land, and they, I think, return that love with something approaching deep respect.

This great sweep of popular support for me has encouraged my fellow politicians and artists on the centre-left to try to find some position in public life suited to my particular talents. The appointment will be announced in the days immediately following a Labour Victory at the next General Election. Neil and Glenys — ordinary, decent folk, both — have had the goodness to suggest that, as the Queen Mother is not getting any younger, I might consider taking her place in the national tapestry when she slides off this mortal coil.

Wearing no more than a sprinkling of light jewellery, and perhaps something sparkly and a touch glamorous as a jacket or blouse, I would engage in short tours of the regions, chatting with factory workers and so forth, waving and smiling a bit, spreading a little happiness, a little comfort, a little warmth where'er I roamed, perhaps reading to orphans and the disabled from my well-loved *Rumpole* series, offering my reassuring opinions on this and that as I tucked into something off the à la carte.

It is a role I have been rehearsing these last thirty years, and which I will accept with all humility.

To the far-flung reaches of Kent to record an edition of *Any Questions?* The audience seems to appreciate my languid humour and my rather droll delivery, coupled with my pleasantly "anti-establishment" opinions, delivered in mercifully aristocratic tones. "I think that Colonel Gaddafi is perfectly beastly," I say, "and Saddam Hussein of Iraq seems to me like an awful prig. But, on a more serious note, Jonathan, might I add that I deplore the killing of innocent people?" This goes down well with the studio audience, who clap and cheer, so I add: "And may I also say how passionately I care for this great country of ours?" Another enthusiastic round of applause. "And one final point: I don't mind admitting that I simply *adore* freedom of speech. Goodnight and God Bless." At the end of the show, the good people in the audience clamour for signed copies of my most recent book, *Rumpole Lunches Again in Tuscany, Volume Five.* An immensely civilised occasion, a far cry from the rooftop protest at Strangeways that has come to symbolise so much of what is wrong with Thatcher's Britain. Prisons are perfectly ghastly places, a bit like I imagine Marbella must be (!) and I would have been on that rooftop myself, had not my attendance at a Foyle's Literary Luncheon been arranged some months ago.

SHIRLEY MACLAINE

We cannot smell with our eyes; our eyes help us to see.

All things come from within us; everything else comes from without.

The dog that barks not is the dog that stays silent.

We feel pain when we are hurt; but when we are not hurt, we feel no pain.

The sparrow sits on the fence. The fence does not sit on the sparrow. But if the fence chooses to sit on the sparrow, the sparrow will find it hard to fly.

I am sitting in a vehicle on Boulevard 909, travelling east on my way to the set of *Postcards from the Edge*, overachieving as usual. My vehicle runs over someone, not a star at all, but an ordinary human being, probably a woman. I love my fellow human beings on the most profound level, so I take the trouble to place my head out the vehicle window. Caringly, I look down to the place where the woman is lying under the wheel. As I see her there, I ponder the intricate impacts we have on one another. Total strangers, yet connected for one short moment in time by a car. Tears well in my eyes as my heart reaches out to her. But I don't want to let her see my *pain*. No, I must use my  inner resources to confront the trauma. "Drive on, please," I say, and as the chauffeur pulls away, and the woman's body recedes into the beautiful infinity of the car mirror, I feel enriched by the strength and resolution I have managed to draw from within. Funny thing, though. In all the minutes that woman was crying out, she never once mentioned loving my performance in *Terms of Endearment*. I guess she is just one of many, many people who are trapped in their own psyches, capable of thinking only of themselves, poor souls.

He who travels furthest must equip himself for the longest voyage.

He who wishes to come back must first go away.

On two legs, a man can walk a mile; but on one leg he must hop.

I am in Cambridge, England. Sitting at the feet of the most beautiful man in the world. Truly. His name? Professor Stephen Hawking. A man who will always be remembered for his literally earth-shattering book *The Time History of Briefs*. What, I am asking myself, am I, one of Hollywood's most celebrated overachievers, with sixty-nine starring movie roles to my credit, not forgetting six profoundly spiritual volumes of auto biography, doing sitting at the feet of this deeply immobilised person? Happily, I'm in communication with my unconscious, always have been, always will be. And the answer comes back: *because he's so beautiful*.

Inquisitive friends — friends searching like me for *meaning* within ourselves — have sometimes asked me what Stephen Hawking and I find to talk about. "A little thing called life," I tell them. "God. Inner oneness. Serendipity. Recognition of the adventure within. Self-discovery."

And here I am, back in Cambridge, England, once again revealing myself to this beautiful human being. "You know,

Stephen," I say. "On a deep soul level, I feel we have met many times before, that I was once your child, and you were my sister. I guess you must feel the same way about me, am I right? Of course I am. And, you know, I believe that in each one of us there is an invisible thread, and that thread is attached to each of the planets in the solar system, and upon each of those marvellous planets sits a perfect, a perfect, a perfect — how shall I put it? — a perfect *replica* of our own inner perfection, and this replica guides us to a state of true love and peace on this planet earth, which, let's face it, Stephen, is the only planet earth we've got, so let's treat it as we would like to be treated ourselves. And you know, reading your beautiful book, I get a strong sense that on the most profound level this is what you yourself have been trying to communicate to the world in print, am I right?"

Poor Stephen. His voicebox seems to have got hopelessly jammed. All that is coming out is a bizarre noise sounding something like "nonononononononono" repeated over and over again. So, looking deeper into his eyes, I reach out to his electric cable and switch it off. "That's better, Stephen," I say. "Now, did I ever tell you my theory about the karma we can achieve through the creative combustion that comes from communicating with trees?"

At this point, Stephen's wheelchair seems to take on a life of its own, moving away from me. "Dear, oh, dear," I say. "We'll have to fix that, won't we?" So I stick a strong stick between the spokes so that it can go no further.

"Perfect," I say. "Now, where were we? Yes — I was about to say how your beautiful book taught me one helluva lot about, of all people, *myself...*"

A bucket contains water, but water does not contain a bucket.

Those who wear shoes on their head must learn to expect blisters on their feet.

The path up the hill is not steep; it is the hill itself that is steep.

Creative artists feel the need to tear back the layers of their psyches. It's like peeling onions, which is why our tears flow so freely, I guess. Long ago, prebirth, I was imbued with the need to strip back the curtain on the mystery of the child within. Creative artists gather together for protection, to participate in the experience of self-discovery; we are always seeking to find out how our fellow artists are *feeling*. "How are you *feeling*?" I asked a good friend last time I saw her. "Only if you're feeling like I'm feeling, well, I guess to be honest I'm trying to come to terms with my capacity to overachieve, and I sometimes think I'm too frail, too sensitive to the fractures of the universe, and I never got to tell my Mom that she loved me, but I'm sorting it all out, my psyche's coping, so I'm glad you're well."

"Yes," replied my friend, my makeup artiste. "But more important, how are *you*?"

"Oh, let's not talk about me," I said, and at that moment I had the sensation of embarking on a great voyage of self-discovery across the valleys and mountains of my innermost projections. "But on the other hand... " I continued.

PEREGRINE WORSTHORNE

Invited to partake of luncheon at the house of a very dear old friend of mine the other day, I was struck by what might best be described as a "contraption", as close as damnit to his telephone. Over an excellent meal of beef in some sort of stew, served, alas, with mediocre wine, I asked my very dear old friend, who has, incidentally, died since — and not before time, the ruthlessly honest might add — exactly what the contraption might be.

"My dear Perry," he replied, for he was extraordinarily fond of me, as I might have been of him had he proved himself more worthy of my affection. "That 'contraption', as you put it, is an 'answer-phone'. It answers the telephone when you are unavailable."

I wonder if anyone else has come across one of these infernal instruments? Can one honestly imagine anyone of the calibre of Plato, Jesus or Prince Albert employing an answer-telephone? I think not. To be sure, my dear old friend will find little use for this absurd machine now that he is dead and buried. Which surely goes to prove its utter uselessness when he was alive.

Has anybody else noticed quite how many young people seem content to walk around on the streets? I would say that well over a third of the people I see on the streets are under the age of twenty-five. Doubtless many of these are perfectly innocent, but I sense that they are all in some way or other involved in street crime of a particularly vicious hue, either in the active or the passive sense. Of course, there would be the usual whines and squeaks from the *Guardian* fraternity were these young people to be interned, but should we allow justice to act as the handmaiden to fashion? I think not. The internment of all those under the age of twenty-five, with suitable provision, of course, for babes-in-arms, albeit those with cast-iron alibis, will appeal to every British bobby worth his salt, and, as such, should prove attractive to all other law-abiding citizens, forsooth.

In these modern times, people go to quite extraordinary lengths to avoid upsetting dwarves, or "little folk", as we are no doubt expected to call them. If one passes a dwarf in the street, it seems one is forbidden by an unspoken taboo to pass comment on his lack of inches, however noticeable and indeed objectionable that lack may be. I am no dwarf — far from it, my friends tell me that I am of a perfect height — but if I were, I would resent such pussy-footing. Of course, I suppose it is possible to go too far in the other direction — dwarf deportation on any major scale would be unworkable, though one imagines they might profitably be stacked — but henceforth I will make pointed comment along the lines of "Oi! shrimpy!" whenever I see one scuttle past my ankles. Dwarves would be the first to admit that they do not respond well to obsessive mollycoddling. Only by such frank and honest means will the dwarf population regain the dignity that is their due. And the example would be chastening to others who might even now be entertaining the temptation to shrink.

The surliness of the London bus-driver knows no bounds. At the weekend, I boarded a Number 14 bus, paid the fare requested, and, with due politeness, asked the driver to turn his vehicle around and transport me to the house of a dear friend in Somerset for Sunday luncheon. At the time, I should add, I was carrying a heavy case of non-vintage champagne, and my Somerset friend was a lady of advanced years who has since passed on (much to the amusement of her friends, to whom she always claimed that she would reach 80!). The driver, who was of the black or "coloured" persuasion, steadfastly refused to accede to my bidding, stating that he was bound for "King's Cross", somewhere to the north of London. The "rules" would not allow a diversion to Somerset. Even after ten years of Mrs Thatcher, there are still, it would appear, areas of public life hamstrung by the rulebook. How very saddening.

I wonder if anyone else has come across the modern expression, much employed by the young of all classes: "Piss off, you pompous old fart"? Nowadays, I seem to hear it where'er I go. At a tupperware party given by very old and dear friends, who, to general merriment, have fallen on hard times, no less than three attractive, well-spoken young ladies practised the expression on me in the course of half an hour. I suspect that it denotes keen approbation of stylish and witty argument, in much the same way that "By jove, you're onto a corker!" did to my generation. Another puzzler is the popular catchphrase, "Up yours", oft heard when one offers a word of advice and the loan of one's hair-comb to the more unkempt of the nation's football "supporters". It seems reasonable to suspect that it is some sort of plaudit for one's command of paradox, spritely turn of phrase, and so on. But why, then, is it so frequently followed by a swift boot to one's shins?

★ STAR THOUGHTS ★

KEITH WATERHOUSE

I note the incorrigible dauber Francis Bacon has finally breathed his last. Shame, because he was by all accounts a cheery cove, never slow to dip into his pocket for a round of ale and pies. But what of his paintings, I hear you ask. Frankly, they remind me of the look on my old Aunt Dolly's face when she found that her piggy-bank had been raided by Uncle Arthur for a flutter on the 1936 Grand National.

But then my old Aunt Dolly could have taught (never *teached*, if you please) Bacon a thing or two about painting. Her own canvas, "Cows Grazing in Pastures Pleasant", won the 2nd Prize at the local Church Fête back in the late Twenties. There are precious few pastures in Bacon, none of them pleasant, and, as for his cows, they're more likely to be hanging on a hook from a ceiling than chewing the proverbial cud.

Perhaps if Bacon had painted a little bit more like my Aunt Dolly he would have been enjoyed more by those many millions of ordinary folk who couldn't give a fig about modern "art" but who like something nice for the wall. Mind you, his bank manager wasn't exactly complaining!

Graffiti spotted on a wall: DOWN WITH FEMALE'S THEIR ORL TART'S. This made me so hopping mad that I got out my trusty felt-tip and corrected it to DOWN WITH FEMALES. THEY'RE ALL TARTS. Thus my campaign for a better-educated Britain continues apace.

SIMON BATES

Betcha didn't expect Simes, Simey, Simon, Si — call me what you will — to be penning the diary "slot" in the *Eye* (aye! aye!) this week. Well, *Private* (more like Public!!) *Eye*'s a funny mag, and I guess I'm widely known as a funny guy, so whaddyaknow, the "Ed" has put two and two together and come up with four — or is it five? — no, but seriously, let's go straight into a great, fun-packed, Radio One style Diary — wayheyhey!

I guess not many of you need telling who I am; but for those of you who are deaf — only joking, honest! — here goes. I'm what they call in the industry a disc-jockey or "jock", and I rule the national airwaves three hours a day, five days a week, come rain or whatever on national Radio One. Sounds like fun, maybe, but I try to be just that little bit serious too. You see, in life, there's tears as well as laughter. There are mountains and there are valleys. You have your ups, you have your downs. One guy doesn't necessarily feel exactly the same as another guy. Some things simply aren't black and white, but a shade of grey. There are blokes and there are ladies, and sometimes they fall in love, and sometimes they don't, so there you go. So let me just say this. I get a little sick of the constant knockers who make out that we DJs don't have a lot of grey matter between our eyes. 'Nuff said.

You know, there are some things that money can't buy. Love. Compassion. A little human understanding. And you know what? They're the most precious things of all.

I guess all of you know by now that last year I went on a marathon trip around the world in just eighty — that's eight zero — days. I visited over fifty different countries, and I sent my thoughts and reflections back via satellite to all the literally millions of listeners to Radio One. The Beeb — in their wisdom! — are bringing out a hefty tome to mark the event containing some of my most memorable comments. My descriptions tended to be very — how shall I put it? — descriptive — so I'd like to reprint some of them here — plug! plug! — as a "taster".

Batesy on Japan: "One helluva fantastic country, this."

Batesy on Australia: "They mainly talk English here, which helps!"

Batesy on the USA: "You know, it's not till you get here that you realise quite how big this country is. It's quite literally very very big indeed."

Batesy on France: "Well, you can't get much more French than this."

Batesy on Eastern Europe: "The vast majority of Eastern Europe can be found over towards the East of Europe, and this probably accounts for the feeling of being more in the East that you pick up here."

Batesy on the International Situation: "You know, sometimes I just wish all the blokes at the top would say, 'Hey, I've got one or two good ideas, and I guess you must have a few, so why not let's get our heads together and make this world a better place.' So, come on, fellas — how about it?"

Batesy on Spain: "You can't get much more Spanish than Spain."

Between these four walls, they're predicting a number one when the book's released in time for Christmas — so start saving, gang!

I guess the most popular feature on national Radio One must be the "My Tune" slot on — yes, you've guessed it — the Simon (that's me, folks!) Bates Show. If you're one of the three fellas in this country who's yet to tune in, let me explain in words of one whatsit what it's all about. Listeners send me in their life stories, a lotta them kinda tragic, kinda sad, and I sift through every one of 'em till I've found one that says it all. It might be a fella who meets this lady who dies in a car-crash and then meets another lovely lady who doesn't wanna commit herself so he gets kinda depressed and does himself in and the lovely lady then finds the right bloke, and they get on pretty well, then their kid is found guilty of murdering a senior citizen, and the bloke takes to drink and beats his lady up in a way that's not at all nice but these things happen and they go through one helluva lot but in the end they still get a lotta pleasure from listening to Chris de Burgh's *Lady in Red* which got to number one in July 1986, so the story has some kinda happy ending I guess; or it may be some other story along the same lines but equally tragic and always with a nice tune to round it off. Beeyoodivul.

C ongratulations are in order to everyone who's doing their bit to make this world a better place. Well done, fellas. You know, nothing's ever quite as bad as it seems,

what goes up must come down, it's love that makes the world go round and, what's more, you can't make an omelette without breaking eggs, so Simon Says keep up the good work.

T hey're a great bunch of guys down at "Auntie Beeb", none greater than my fellow Radio One jocks. Every now and then we have a bit of a get-together, a bit of a chin-wag, how's-your-father, what-you-will, exchange a few laughs, that sort of thing. We had one helluva time a few nights back — kissagrams, the lot — but that would be telling! You know, some of the guys on Radio One are so sharp that I've started keeping notes for a book of Witty Remarks by Radio One Deejays. It's early days yet, but I've already clocked these little gems: "The time's just coming up to ten-thirty-five on National Radio One, time for some Weather News" (Simon Mayo); "In my opinion, the new track by Phil Collins is just great, for what it's worth, and from such a genuine bloke, too" (Gary Davies), and "You know, for some people it never rains but it pours" (Simon Bates — whoops! caught blowing my own trumpet again!). Anyway, I've just got time to say goodbye for now, see you soon, goodbye, 'bye, see you tomorrow, cheerio, ta-ra, 'bye for now. 'Bye.

MELVYN BRAGG

Came in for a bit of a pasting from the *Private Eye* "literary" "critic" (note the quotes!) last issue, but no hard feelings, if that's how he has to earn his cash, good luck to him, poor lad, but I'd like to take this opportunity to point out that as long ago as 1973 the distinguished critic Francis King described me as — and I quote — "almost as good as any other young Cumbrian novelist of his generation". High praise indeed, and for my money worth a lot more than the jealous carpings of the ever-present "anon". Anyway, I'm most grateful to everyone at the *Eye* for giving me this chance to reply. Thanks chaps. Love the mag. Cheers.

A new novel out, another round of interviews. Actually, the new one's a bit of a departure. Deals with sexual obsession, which, interestingly, puts me in a line of writers from Hazlitt to Nabokov to Updike, not that I'm trying to put myself in that category, though future literary "buffs" might well come round to that belief, who's to say. A writer though, is basically what I am. I like a sentence well-turned to be. And with rhythm. Plus inner music.

To write about the sexual act requires great sensitivity from a leading contemporary novelist such as myself, and one's writing must go beyond the realm of cliché and into the world of poetry, because, let's face it, sex is the greatest thing since sliced bread.

Let me demonstrate what I mean by quoting, if I may, from my own latest novel, complex, sensitive, intriguing, occasionally difficult but ultimately rewarding, *You Got A Nice Pair There, Love* (Hodder £12.95, 220pp). It deals in a compassionate and strangely tender way with the sexual affair between a fifty-year-old man called Martin Bloggs and a young girl less than half his age. Strong stuff, but in the hands of a master craftsman it is, as you can see, transformed into something strangely sensuous.

"I love you, Martin Bloggs," you said, clutching my left buttock in the nobbly bit of your ankle, you know the bit I mean, the bit that sticks out, roughly two inches from the heel. "And I love you too, Thingy." I gasped as your eyelash brushed against my khaki anorak, well, sort of more green than khaki really.

Wild, tender, firm, luscious, energetic, juicy. That ham sandwich you made me was first class, love. And our love-making was first class too, lasting for two hours and twenty-three minutes, right the way through Coronation Street, *straight on through* Only Fools and Horses *and well into* Panorama.

My hand felt for yours, I clutched it tight, caressing it, feeling it against the small of my back, you know, that bit that sometimes gives me cause for complaint. Together, our hands became one, one hand with ten fingers and no palm and two wrists. I was reaching the top of the cliff, the upper floor of the tower-block, the luggage-rack of the motor vehicle. Suddenly, I saw your face towering above me. You had just returned to the room after nipping out for some beans on toast. It was my own hand that I had been clutching all along.

With one deft movement, you removed your motor-cycle helmet. I had never seen you like that before. "Your hair!" I exclaimed. "Your hair is of medium length." That just about said it all.

The book is set in Cumbria, where my roots are. I'm not really a television "personality", you see. I prefer to see myself as an ordinary bloke, scratching a living. I always try to return to Cumbria whensoe'er I can, to tread the fells, to feel the earth's heartbeat pounding through my very soul, to pass banter with my ain folk, to fill my lungs with the rich, mountain air, to set to work with a trowel and dig up my roots once more. I managed to get back there for a weekend last year, and this year I'm promising myself the full three days. I describe the landscape most movingly in this passage from my forthcoming follow-up to *The Maid of Buttermere*, provisionally titled *The Pat of Flora*. An historical novel, it concerns the fate of an 18th-century television producer, inexorably drawn back to his beloved Cumbria, single-mindedly dedicated to proving to the world that he is a real person.

The sun crept up from over the horizon like a welder donning his long-johns prior to a busy day down the mines, poor sod. Merlin Bogg, on good money these days, watched as the clouds stretched their wings and flew, flew, flew, hither and thither amongst the trees, tweeting and chirruping like ten thousand goshawks, all fluttering about like so many clouds, which is what they were. The rain poured down like... like... like

so much rain. Bad weather, perchance, but Bogg was determined to weather it. Nowt to complain of. That just about said it all.

No doubt the carpers will criticise me for quoting so extensively from one of my own books, and good luck to 'em, but I wanted to show just how my creative life has been deeply influenced by my intimate knowledge of the Cumbrian countryside in and around the area of Torquay.

Of course, I now spend most of my time in Hampstead, attracted by its close-knit Cumbrian community. In a funny sort of way, the gleam from the spotlights in the wine bars and boutiques of Hampstead High Street sends my mind reeling back to the glint of sun on the Windermere of my youth, the sparkle in me old Nan's eyes as she called us in for our bread and stout. These days, I make no secret of the fact that I am a stalwart Labour Party Gold Card Member, contributing as hard as dammit for a Labour victory come election time. If Neil and Glenys — lovely lady — choose to repay my support with a knighthood and Chairmanship of the Arts Council, then so be it, I'll be only too glad to do my bit. Until then, I'll keep forging those novels on the anvil of my plough. I'll furrow a ford through life's gateposts, and I'll celebrate, in prose, my roots in my Lloyds syndicate, actually could you change that to Cumbria, thanks love, that's enough words for today, fancy a drink?

THE RT HON NEIL KINNOCK MP

That was a fabulous trip I had to the Unified States of America, really fabulous. Incredible, really. Fantastic. We drove up to the White House, huge place, really, in a big car — sizeable boot, four doors, electronic windows, little flag in front, the trimmings — and found ourselves shaking hands with the President of the Unified States, Mr George Bush, lovely man. Fan-bloody-tastic.

Of course, one has to dress up for these historic occasions, so I had brought over a couple of my best double-breasteds, leaving the final choice to that morning, depending on mood. Finally, I chose the one with the very slight flare, because I wanted to empha-sise the Labour Party's modern, forward-looking approach. Cuffs, too, are important, I find, and I have my tailor pin on especially enlarged, detachable cuffs, so as to heighten my statesman-ship. Finally, a tie. You can't meet the President without a tie, oh no, matey. I selected the Carmarthen and District Rugby Union Supporters Tie, as my ad-visers had informed me that Mr George Bush was something of a sporting fel-low and I thought it might "break the ice". To be quite honest, perfectly frank and straight down the line with you, when the time came he didn't actually mention the tie, though he must have seen it. Odd really.

Talking of "breaking the ice", I'm a dab hand at it myself, and I soon got the President chuckling, I can tell you.

As we were introduced and we were shaking hands and he was admiring my cuffs and my fabulous suit and so on, I said to him, I said, "Your name's Bush, I take it", to which he replied that, yes, it was. "Well, George," I quipped, "back in Wales, we have an old saying, 'A bird in the hand is worth two in the *Bush*'!!"

To be utterly open with you, the "quip" wasn't an instant success, but more of a slow burn. The President kept shaking my hand and smiling while he discreetly turned to his adviser and whis-pered out of the side of his mouth: "Get me a translator — fast."

"No need," I laughed. "Let me ex-plain that little bit of a joke for you. You see, the word 'Bush' back in Britain means a little tree or shrub, usually green, or at any rate green-ish, and you know what a bird is, presumably..." And so I talked him through the "play on words", and by the end of it he was smiling hard. This left us with a clear ten minutes for defence policy, NATO, EMS and other major issues, which we both found more than enough, being busy men.

America. What a country, eh? Fabulous. Oddly enough, I discovered that the capital of America is not New York, as you'd expect, but Washington. I'm a bit of a trivia nut, as you can tell!

What a lovely lady Mrs Bush is, too, really lovely and very easy to talk to, I found. Again "breaking the ice", I said to her: "My wife, Glenys, is a great fan of your husband's early films." You see, you shouldn't spend all day talking international statesmanship, you've got to present a "human" side, especially to the lovely ladies. To be absolutely frank, Barbara — that's her Christian name, her surname being "Bush" like her husband's — looked a little blank before saying very nicely that she didn't realise her husband had actually made any films. Astonishing, eh? Here that lovely lady was, married to a guy who'd acted in, ooh, hundreds of great Westerns, and she had no idea. Anyway, I rattled off a few titles Glenys had particularly enjoyed, describing the odd scene from them as well — at one point getting Gerald Kaufmann, who was with me, to act the part of the Red Indian squaw — and she found it most informative. "I must try and catch up on them," she told me, delightedly, before leaving the room for an urgent appointment.

T alking of the EMS — that's the European Money Sentre — I've been attacking the Government on it and related issues with all the power, vigour and force at my disposal, and I've noticed, though I say it myself, that they've been quite taken aback by my command of the subject. What they don't realise — and I've been keeping it up my sleeve — is that my second best subject at school was Sums. Long division, multiplication, geography, distraction, you name it. So when you next see Maggie reel from one of my swift, fast, speedy, quick and instantaneous rapier blows, verbal punches or thrusts, you can think of the young Kinnock (that's me, folks!) doing his tables (eight sevens are fifty-three, nine sevens are sixty-two, etc, etc) at his old school desk in Bedwelty all those years ago. Amazing, really, when you think that without those sums

I wouldn't be where I am today, i.e., Leader of the Opposition!

I t's taken a few thumps and one or two tears, I can tell you, but the Labour Party now has a coherent and adhesive set of policies with which to enter the next election. We are committed to Home Ownership. We are against Secondary Picketing. We are fully committed to Europe. We are in favour of competition. We are fully supportive of a sound nuclear defence policy. We see no value in the old dinosaurs of state monopolies. We have pledged our allegiance to the Royal Family and the wonderful traditions it represents. We can see no reason why the entrepreneur should be penalised for taking the initiative. We wish to work hand in hand with America. And yet still some people tell us that we are not a viable alternative to Thatcherism!

W hat a lovely, lovely guy Nelson Mandela is. Very warm and considerate gentleman, you can take it from me. Glenys and me had the great privilege — for that is what it was — of meeting the man himself on his recent visit to this country. It was a great thrill to sit with him in the Royal Box at Wembley for a truly magnificent evening of pop music. And do you know what he said to me at the end? He said: "I've always wanted to meet you. I'm one of your biggest fans." The great Mandela one of *my* biggest fans! I literally couldn't believe it! "Yes," added his charming wife, Winnie. "And he particularly likes your version of *Something In The Air Tonight* and all the early Genesis." Fabulous couple, really fabulous.

ANTONIA FRASER

Napkins, or serviettes, continue to be a problem. One was always brought up to believe that they were indispensable at all times, and one's father would invariably use one while masticating. Harold prefers to employ the back of his hand, so that at the close of one of our important socialist discussion groups — of which more later — he has numerous gobbets of smoked salmon sandwich embedded between the masculine hairs that sprout so luxuriantly from his wrist. Of course, the servants, absolute dears, are immensely grateful for these gobbets — needless to say they simply *adore* smoked salmon! — but I still maintain that the use of a sturdy napkin, or serviette, would ensure that these little treats could be popped into the servants' mouths free from excess hair. I would be interested to know what readers think.

Still on the napkin, or serviette, problem: should one place them any-old-how beside each setting at a dinner party, or should one attempt to construct something a little more artistic? A month or so ago, we enjoyed the company of President Daniel Ortega as a houseguest, and I insisted before his arrival that we should turn our napkins, or serviettes, into marvellous "fighting fists", to show our solidarity with his delicious struggle in Barbados. Daniel, who, con-

trary to what one hears in the right-wing press, is an absolute poppet, was tremendously touched. In Barbados, he told us, the freedom fighters must do without napkins, or serviettes, so they would be especially touched by my small (and to my mind hopelessly inadequate) gesture. The very next day, I nipped out to Peter Jones and ordered 300,000 paper napkins, or serviettes — one for each of his marvellous Sindinastis, and I have made it quite clear that they mustn't all waste their precious time writing thank-you letters. We must each of us do what we can to help the cause, Harold says.

With all due respect to politics, one must never neglect one's literature, like it or not. I am at present engaged in writing a super biography of someone from the olden days, and I am also busy compiling an anthology called *Ordinary Blokes with Hearts of Gold: The Working Classes in Literature*, which is the wonderful idea of my great friend George Weidenfeld. George it was who steered me through my other best-selling anthologies, *Of Posies and Petticoats: Nice Things from Books* and *Second Helpings: Lady Antonia Fraser selects her Favourite Meals from Great Literature*. George thinks that it would be an excellent idea to get a real member of the working-class to write an introduction, so I have been racking my brains. At the moment, we've only been able to come up with Arthur Mullard or Major "Ron" Ferguson, but any other suggestions would be more than welcome.

When a small but exclusive group of distinguished people agreed to hold informal socialist discussion groups, we little expected the torrent of abuse and sheer bad manners that would rain down upon us. Our inaugural dinner took place at a marvellous little restaurant, The

River Café in darkest Hammersmith. A stimulating evening indeed. Jonathan (Raban) kicked off the discussion by pointing out that his Ramekin of Escalopes of Duck Foie Gras in a Muscat Sauce had cost almost as much as the weekly Child Benefit awarded to an unmarried mother with two kiddies, "and I still haven't had my main course". David (Hare) was equally gloomy about the state of Thatcher's Britain. "It makes me sick to think that this Mille-Feuille of Baby Lobster served in a Light Mangetout Sauce with an accompanying salad of Roquefort, Avocado and Croutons on a Bed of Black Walnuts represents a day and a half's pay to a Grade Two Ambulance Driver. What the hell can we do about it, that's what I'd like to know?" By this time, tears were streaming down his cheeks. "Perhaps if we had a little word with the Manager," suggested John (Mortimer), "he could wangle us a bit of a discount for our next group booking."

The June 20th Group has since disbanded, for we have achieved most of our aims. When the rest of the country realised that figures of the calibre of John (Mortimer) and Melvyn (Bragg) were thinking Left-wing thoughts, they all wanted to follow suit, and now, thanks in no small part to us, Mrs Thatcher is well down in the polls. But we still make the effort to give over the odd evening to entertaining Neil and Glenys. To set them at their ease, I tend to eschew my normal silks for more down-to-earth "overalls", and we serve what I believe are known as "chip butties" with lashings of "custard", though it suits me to eat something else later. What a sweet couple they are! After they have finished the washing-up, I always insist on pressing some small change into their hands, but they won't hear of it. Harold and I simply can't wait for them to be

★ STAR THOUGHTS ★
BUBBLES ROTHERMERE

What a hectic life one leads! Yesterday, I had my hair done in the morning and I ordered some new curtains in the afternoon, as well as going to a super, super party in the evening. It's literally all go. How one longs sometimes for a quiet, simple life like the little people who work in supermarkets must enjoy! Instead, one works ceaselessly for others, bringing a little sunshine into their lives just by *being there*.

My charity work continues apace. I am on the committee for next season's Ethiopian Famine Dinner (fingers crossed that they hold a famine in Ethiopia next season, or all our hard slog goes up the spout quite frankly!). I am also up to my knees in gorgeous Green campaigns like stopping everyone using lead-free petrol, closing down the Ozone Layer and making everyone put baby seals to good use, like wearing them.

the next little people in Number Ten!

Of course, Harold was himself born slightly "working class" (incidentally, what a beastly term that is!), but you wouldn't guess it now. Occasionally, one of his "little ways" comes back — at dinner the other night at Clarence House he flew into one of his "rages" about I-don't-know-what and challenged the Queen Mother to an arm-wrestling contest — but otherwise you couldn't tell. And I'm delighted to say that, come January 1st, he has promised to employ a napkin, or serviette, and to refrain from terming it a "snotrag". Happy New Year!

CAROL AND MARK THATCHER

Coooeee! Carol T. here, daughter of Mummy! Me and Mark are penning the diary in this scuwillous journal this week — for our sins!! — but first offs we'd like to make it clear that we are doing it (actually we're not doing it as such, we're only bro and sis — joke!!) so as to waise the public pwofile of The Thatcher Foundation, a charity organisation set up to let everyone know about the super ideas that mummy has, such as the Community Charge and entering a wecession and not liking Europe. We aim to keep you tewiffically entertained, but we also aim to get you to dig jolly deep into those pockets for a weally super cause. Over to you, Marky!

Thanks, Carol. There's one popular misconception I'd like to clear up pretty damn pronto, okay? I am not — repeat, not — any kind of "shady dealer" who is into "making money" by "riding on his mother's back". Glad to have pulled the plug on that one.

I guess there will be those who want verification. Fair enough. Ask my mother, Mrs Margaret Thatcher, ex-Prime Minister of Great Britain and still a leading figure of world influence with contacts everywhere. Between these four walls, if you want to check that out with her in person, I could see my way clear to arranging a one-to-one meeting on very attractive terms, cash callers only please.

Absolutely super offer there, Mark! Carol here again, chums! My talents are in the way I can write about things so that readers who can read my writing can really understand what that writing means and i suppose that's because my talents are in the way i write. Like Mark, I absolutely wefuse to "cash in" on mummy's name, and I've got countless articles and books written under my own name to pwove it, i.e.*Diary of an Election — On the Road With Mummy by Carol Thatcher* (1983), "Carol Thatcher On What It's Like Being Mummy's Daughter" (*Sunday Express*, '81, '84, '85, '87, '88–'91) and "The Joy of Bobsleighing by Carol Thatcher" (*Daily Mail*, '89). The latter article started quite bwilliantly: "You don't have to be the Prime Minister's daughter to feel a gweat wush of adwenalin as you go jolly fast downhill in a Bobsleigh — but it helps!" Good stuff, eh, Mark?

Right, Carol. On a more serious note, commentators are claiming that this is a bad time for business but not from where I'm standing it bloody isn't. Just yesterday, I made a cool 30g. without setting foot outside my luxury suite at Claridges, and that can't be bad, no way José.

Y'know, people sometimes ask me how exactly I earn my crust. Good question, and it deserves a good answer. Basically, I'm a people person. I bring people together and set up an attractive business environment in which they feel able to operate. I'll throw you a f'rinstance, if I may. Say you have a

Scud missile on your hands — and I'm only saying *if*, please note — and you want to find a good home for it, you think: "Hmm, must contact my old friend Marky, he'll know the right bloke" and you give me a bell toot-sweet. Are you still with me? Marky here then flicks through his trusty contacts book and finds a marvellous old character, perhaps from the Middle East, who's simply crying out for such a first-class weapon. Bob's your proverbial, and in a jiffy hands are being shaken, contracts exchanged and a nice bit of vintage fizzy stuff on ice is wheeled in, courtesy Executive Room Service. Okay, so it's hard work, but I've never been frightened of that, and I've always wanted to be independent of my mother who is, incidentally, Mrs Margaret Thatcher, no less! Back to you, Carol.

Nice to have that cleared up for us, Mark. Sounds jolly interesting, I must say. As you all know, I'm a top journalist specialising in pwetty over-the-top assignments! You could say that I'm always "game for a laugh", to coin a phwase, and that's why Fleet Street's top editors are always on the blower to me. "Here's an assignment requiring someone to throw themselves off a cliff," they gasp. "I know, let's send top journalist Carol Thatcher!"

In my writing style I try hard to convey the breathless excitement of everything that happens to me in a manner that is very exciting and makes my excited weaders weally excited by the exciting things that happen to me and to feel it was almost as if they were doing these exciting things for themselves though they are obviously not, they are only reading about them.

Only last year, when I wang my chums at the *Daily Mail* and asked them if they had any super daredevil assignment for yours truly they asked me to go

take a wunning jump, which weally got my adwenalin flowing, I kid you not! The very next day, I was climbing up the famous Swiss Matterhorn weady to throw myself off so as to be able to describe it for my devoted following of weaders. Let's take a peek at how I captured that amazing moment:

"Taking a running jump is what one might call quite something or at least those were the thoughts that ran through my head as I plunged over the side of the Matterhorn. The feeling was literally indescribable, so much so that even now I can't describe it. 'That,' I told my super ambulanceman, 'was literally indescribable.' And if there's a single word that sums up the whole experience it was that one word. Literally indescribable."

And so to business. Why not treat yourself to the gift of a lifetime and take up exclusive membership of The Thatcher Foundation (all major credit cards accepted)? Membership will entitle you to full use of leisure facilities — solarium, members' pool, cocktail lounge, etcetera — at no extra cost to you or your family, and with the optional extra of a welcoming drink with yours truly plus wife and family (optional extra). My mother will, of course, be on hand during the day to give you the benefit of her views on a variety of world issues, perhaps over a glass of our sensational Fruit Punch.

To take the kid gloves off for half a mo: we're after a cool 50g per institution, 5g per individual, straight up, no questions asked, and for an extra 25g we'll throw in a piece of state-of-the-art military hardware, can't say fairer than that. 'Nuff said, but do let's try to honour my mother by giving as much as you can to this smooth and stylish monument. Checks payable to "M. Thatcher". Ciao for now. Ciao!

SIR ROY STRONG

People can be such absolute poppets. They so often come up to me and say, "Roy," they say, "Roy, how can *we* become half as *gifted* and *stylish* as you?"

One has to let them down lightly, of course, but then no one, *but no one*, is beyond *some* improvement. "You'll have to get rid of that perfectly *dreadful* suit for a start," I might say. "And are you really telling me that no one has had a word with you about your face?"

They're very grateful for these few words of advice, but it's an uphill struggle, it really is. I'll always remember what dear darling Diana Cooper once said to me. "Roy," she said, "Roy, how I wish that I could look like you! But I can't, and I will somehow have to learn to live with it!" Towards the end of her life, I do believe she became reconciled, if only partially, to this one great regret, though I believe she was occasionally seen wandering The Ritz forlornly, wearing a specs-nose-and-moustache mask, desperate that someone — *anyone* — should mistake her for me.

I am, as everyone knows, utterly passionate about gardening. But I'm revealing no secrets when I say that dirt can play *absolute havoc* with one's fingernails. I remember my manicurist growing hopping mad when I told him that I was intent on fifteen minutes of hard graft *au jardin*. "Sir Roy," he said, "Sir Roy, you'll *ruin* those follicles!"

It goes without saying that his dire warning sent shivers down my spine, but "Chin up, Roy" I told myself (incidentally, I always drop the title when talking to myself — it makes one feel so much more *relaxed*), "you're going to be terribly, terribly brave." I can tell you now, I stood looking at that trowel for a good few hours, stiff with worrying whether that perfectly beastly dirt would penetrate the three pairs of gloves I was wearing. "Big breath, Roy, big breath," I eventually said to myself, plunging into the ground with gusto, managing to make quite a little dent in it, though one says it oneself.

Returning to the safety of one's Georgian Rectory, one removed one's gloves and went at one's hands with the Crabtree and Evelyn like the blazes, until there was absolutely *no trace anywhere* of ghastly grubbiness. Incidentally, I'll always remember something my fellow diarist, my very dear friend the Queen Mum said to me in this context. As always, she was looking positively radiant, straight out of Botticelli. "I would *adore* to hear your gardening tips," I ventured, setting her at her ease. "*Do tell!*" "And this is Dr Strong, Keeper of the Victoria and Albert Museum, ma'am," said her Lady-in-Waiting. "How do you do?" she replied, before moving on, and I find those lovely words ringing in my ears whenever the garden appears to "get on top of one".

I have, as everyone knows, a very famous cat indeed called The Reverend Wenceslas Muff (!) who is, I might add, among my greatest fans. I find that a lot of people say to me, "Oh, but Sir Roy, what a simply *marvellous* name! How did you possibly come up with anything so *witty!*"

If the truth of the matter be known, the name of The Reverend Wenceslas Muff (!) was decided by a special committee of my very dearest supporters among the staff of the V&A, cat lovers all, over an exquisite *smorgasbord*. I gave them express instructions that they were to submit for my inspection no less than five names. Those names, I announced, should be reflective of the sometimes enigmatic but never less than fascinating nature of my larger-than-life personality, and each of them should have something of a liturgical flavour. Then I "left them to it", as it were, retiring to my executive chaise-longue in order to give my moustache a well-earned rest.

Returning to the fray three hours later, I was delighted to find that they had, at last, finalised the short-list, the five suggested names being:

a) The Reverend Wenceslas Muff
b) Canon Simpering Screamer
c) Monsignor Tetchy Old Queen
d) Bishop Blubbering Bumboy
e) The Rt Reverend Pompous Twat

Of the five suggestions, I chose the first, finding in it a delicious combination of the cultured and the cosy, a delightfully *civilised* title for any self-respecting feline friend. It was only later that one of the lower orders with whom I rub shoulders in my "keep-fit" sessions at the local gymnasia informed me that "Wenceslas Muff" is in fact an ancient naval term meaning "Moustachioed Woofter", but by then he wouldn't answer to anything else.

Current favourite flowers: magnolia, japonica, fuchsia, Queen Mum.

One is so often asked to contribute to features about oneself that one can grow positively *exhausted*. There are, alas, so few people around these days with any sense of style and *oomph* that editors are simply *begging* for my services.

On a Woden's Day morn not three months ago, one had just finished one's breakfast of three Poppy Seeds (we have these flown in fresh from *Milano*) when one was summoned to that most *galling* of modern contraptions, the telephonic communicator (!), by one's little woman. On the other end of the electric wire was a very enthusiastic young researcher from something called *The Late Show* who couldn't have been more super concerning one's achievements. "We would *so* absolutely love it if you'd appear, you're *just* the man we need, you'd be *so completely perfect, do* say you will!"

Hey-ho. One does like to cooperate, so one felt frankly duty-bound to reply in the affirmative. Oddly enough, though she told me that the programme was to be transmitted this very evening, I can find it nowhere in what I believe are known as the schedules. All my daily newspaper (the *Independent* for preference *s'il vous plaît*) tells one about tonight's *Late Show* is "New-Wave Ceramicists; interview with Milan Kundera; Kevin Coyne in the studio; special feature on forgotten Sixties figures with little round specs and gaucho moustaches", and obviously none of those headings applies to me, unless, of course, I am — perish the thought — Milan Kundera!!!

THE RT HON CECIL PARKINSON MP

It is a very great pleasure for me to be given this opportunity to put forward the Government's position on a number of important topics. Very kind people — some of them attractive young ladies! — tell me that I am what they call a "natural communicator". I accept the compliment with grace. If I have such a quality, it derives from my great belief in this Government's frankly first-rate policies, and the terrific team we now have. All I have to do is to state these great assets clearly and smoothly, and the next election will be ours, and it is indeed gratifying to think that I can do the "communicating" job better than, say, John Selwyn Gummer, that slimy little twerp about time she got rid of him and as for that bloody Howe and if that Baker does that smile once more I'll kill him the bastard. To employ a nautical expression, with a steady hand such as mine on the anchor all should be well.

I have always considered what I call "personal grooming" to be of overriding importance. I have long held to the opinion that if people can't respect your hairstyle then you equally can't ask them to respect your policies. Luckily, I have a very full head of hair, and I'm happy to report that the compliments tend to flood in concerning its body, general tidiness and overall grooming. Might I seize this opportunity to pass on a few tips?

a) Do remember to wear a hair-net upon retiring to bed. I regret to say that a number of my Cabinet colleagues — first-rate team, incidentally — have overlooked this advice, resulting in flyaway hair, poor quality partings and general lack of body. Small wonder that Lawson went for the proverbial Burton. I know he'll forgive me for saying this — Nigel's a very old friend of mine, and I have the greatest respect for his now alas gravely discredited economic abilities — but his hair was often disorderly and never anywhere near as spruce as mine. Why? Simple. He forgot his hair-net. So much for the fat slug, who is, incidentally, a much-valued colleague and old friend of myself and my loyal wife Ann.

b) I never forget to place a seawater fish — cod or turbot are both readily available from your high street fishmonger — underneath my hair-net before "turning in for the night". The excellent oils and aromatic properties permeate from the fish through into the hair and scalp to afford perfect manageability in the morning, and my steadfast wife Ann is more than grateful for a cod lunch around mid-day, first removing any of my stray hairs from the gills, of course.

I am delighted to have been given this opportunity to show you what one might call the more "human" side of "yours truly". It can be a great burden, you know, to be lumbered with the title of "the great communicator", as it prevents people from seeing the more warm and rather private side of what has been described as my "terrific personality". You'll no doubt be wondering how I came by the above knowledge of personal grooming for men. Before entering the worlds of industry and politics, I served an apprenticeship at a prestige gentlemen's hairdressing salon in South Audley Street. As well as learning the finer points of trimming, perming, pruning and so on, one received a valuable education in how to present oneself in an attractive manner while looking in the mirror at one's client. Nowadays, when I am asked by the Prime Minister to present the "human face" of the Party on the small screen, I pretend to myself, as the studio manager "cues in", that I am back in that salon, with the camera as the mirror and you, the great British electorate, as my client. As you can judge for yourself, this works beautifully, though I think Peter Sissons might have been a little surprised at the close of a recent *Question Time* when I found myself asking whether sir required anything for the weekend.

Pedicure is another of my talents, my Diploma taking pride of place on my office wall. It is a skill much valued by the Prime Minister. It was at the end of one of the crisis meetings of the inner Cabinet during the Falklands Conflict that I first suggested to the Prime Minister that she should relax with a pedicure, and she took to it like a duck to water. Now, in our full Cabinet sessions, she takes care to place her Secretary of State for Transport in the chair opposite, so that, when the urge overtakes her, she may throw off a shoe and place her foot under the table in my able hands, all the while holding forth about the grave issues of the day. "Other people bring me problems," she once told a mutual friend, "but Cecil brings me pedicures."

This remark arouses some jealousy amongst my absolutely first-rate team of Cabinet colleagues, of course. Ken Clarke is so ham-fisted he couldn't pick his own nose without first consulting an expert, and that little prick Gummer looks like something you'd file out of a toenail, so my position at the feet of the Prime Minister seems assured.

Might I just put in a word on the need for Cabinet loyalty? 1990 has so far been a particularly trying year for myself and my colleagues in Government, and now, more than ever before, there is a desperate need for Ministerial solidarity. Many of my colleagues, alas, do not abide by these rules, little realising that stray off-the-cuff remarks about, say, Waddington's overpowering body odour could prove most unhelpful.

Happily, I inspire tremendous loyalty from my colleagues, who have thankfully put my little "local difficulty" of 1983 behind them, and are now more anxious than ever that I take the "driving seat" in the run-up to the next election. Cabinet memos confirm this. At the last Cabinet meeting, I intercepted a memo from Clarke to Baker while Margaret was droning on. It was tremendously heartening: "Cecil holds the Keays to the next election!!" it read, to which Baker's memo soon came back, "Conservatives Flor-a Great Victory!!" Soon, Howe had chipped in with a memo of his own stating, "No Flies on Cecil!!" On the evidence of such overwhelming support, I can safely say that any problems I may have had are in the past and that my role in Cabinet can grow stronger.

One final tip, if I may. Kind supporters often ask me how I get my head to bounce about uncontrollably in sudden jerks in that attractive way on television and in Westminster. The answer, of course, is a discreet electric-shock machine secreted in one's collar stud. It serves both to stimulate the hair follicles and to ensure a smile appears in the area of one's mouth every 25–30 seconds, with little or no damage to the brain.

HRH THE DUKE OF YORK

I call it "the bog", like most blokes I know do. Fergs — that's my lady wife, for your info! — says that bog is common, and that I should either call it "lavvy" or, for preference, "little boys' room". What I say is, what does it matter what you call the blessed thing just so long as your bum gets on that seat in time!! Anyway, I'm a Royal, so how can I be common, ducks, I said? John, karzi, toilet, what you will, so long as it flushes, who's worrying?

We had Gazza — Paul Gascoigne, great bloke, take it from me — to dindins the other day at the new house. What a guy! I'll tell you something for nothing, he's just as good at arm-wrestling as he is at footer, as I learnt to my cost (groan)!!! Here's what happened, great story: Gazza pressed the bloody doorbell (brilliant doorbell, actually — plays The Grand Old Duke of York, swank, swank, no kidding — incredible, eh?) and I shouted out that he should just push the door open and march straight in. This he did! And found himself literally drenched in a bucket of soapy water!

Frankly, I can't resist a really great practical joke, call me a big baby! So in he comes, literally drenched, clutching his eight-pack of lager and he challenges me on the spot to an arm-wrestle. Blimey, some arm-wrestle! We go to the dining-room table, clear the china out of the way, and get down to business. Wallop! He has me in one! Whoopsie — Fergie comes in at the sound of all the plates crashing to the ground but by this time yours truly and Gazza are in absolute hysterics! "Men!" she sighs to our other dinner guest, lovely Claire Rayner, rolling her eyes up to the ceiling. "Men!" sighs Claire, and then we all have a really good laugh. Luckily the china was really old, something like two hundred years old I should think, so who's going to miss it? What I always say is, all you need for nosh is your two hands and a good set of choppers — none of this chinky-chinky-china nonsense!

As the whole world knows, I'm a bit of a professional when it comes to photography, though frankly I'm only half as good as photographers who are twice as good as me. A new book of my greatest photographs is planned for the Spring, including a) "Baby Bea's Right Foot plus Bit of Fergie's Hand", b) "Whoops! Who Left the Cap On? (Study in Darkness)" and c) "Horse Running Along Sand (Top Left)". My friends tell me they could have been done by a real amateur, high praise indeed.

I know one helluva lot of our fans want to know a whole lot more about our lovely new home. Fave room? It has to be my Den — or Dirty Den, as Fergs calls it, whoops! It's tucked away in the basement and you know when you come to it because a little plaque says "Andy's Den — No Birds Admitted ('cept maybe Linda Lusardi if she asks nicely!!!)". Inside, there's darts, snooker, bar area (Harp on draught), video library (yes, there is the odd saucy flick, but let's hear no more about *that* if you please!!!) and a full range of pillows, soda-siphons and crazy-foam for what me and my mates call "mucking about".

You've guessed it, Andy's Den also has its very own "smallest room" with a little plaque saying "Andy's Bog — Cor, What a Ponger!!!" My little plaques get everyone going — and I don't mean like that! For a bit of a laugh, I'm even thinking of having the motto on my coat of arms changed to — wait for it — "He Who Supplied It Denied It"!! By the way, did you hear about the smelly Chinaman called Hoo Flung Dung? Bloody brilliant!

Fave food? Steak and chips. Fave newspaper or magazine? *Viz* — bloody amusing, really is. Fave disc-jockey? Simon Bates. He really seems to care, and he exhibits a good sense of humour. Fave gift? Last Christmas, Fergs gave me this amazing pair of Y-Fronts with the slogan "Long Vehicle Ahead" printed on them! Fave pop song? Anything by Phil Collins. Fave hairstyle? For a guy, definitely short: otherwise you can't tell if he's a bloke or a bird! Fave catchphrase? Oy! Oy!

Talking of Crimble, I've been writing a fabby Children's Story to give to my son Beatrice on December 25th. Actually, you've probably realised that I'm the only member of my family who's never written a Children's Story, though Fergs has given me strong hints that her hero "Budgie", who is red and whirring and always getting into mischief, may well be based on a certain part of my anatomy (oy! oy!)!!!

So this year as I say I've written my own kiddies' story called, yes, you've guessed it, *Bobby the Bog Roll*. I read it to Gazza late one night and quite honestly he was in absolute hoots. I'm very proud to be able to announce that the firm of Sinclair Stephenson will be publishing it. Only trouble is, all I've written so far is "Hello, my name is Bobby the Bog Roll" and though they really love it so far they say there's still not quite enough, and a bit more story would help with sales. Any ideas?

"Snog on the Tyne is all mine all mine Snog on the Tyne is all mine". Groan! Sorry! Just my little joke — they keep on coming, folks!!!

One helluva lot of my mates are celebrities — comedians, personalities, the lot. As you know, Bea's godparents include Claire Rayner, Billy Connolly, David Frost and Mike Parkinson, while the godparents to my other son, Eugenie, include England cricketer Mike Gatting, the great Jimmy Greaves, TV funnyman Jim "Nick Nick" Davidson and TV-am weathergirl Trish Williamson. Not surprising then, that I've gained myself something of a reputation as a bit of a jester or "Clown Prince". But, on a more serious note, I get fed up to the back teeth with people who criticise the Royal Family and the bloody good work we do. I wouldn't swap places with us for anything. Frankly, I'd much rather be just an ordinary bloke living in an ordinary ten-up, ten-down with hardly any servants at all and only five or six holidays a year earning my twenty quid a week and having jolly good fun with simple hobbies like walking, running, hopping, standing.

Fave sign spotted in the back of a car? "Honk If You've Had It Today"! Had *what*, I wonder???!!!! Oy! Oy! Cheers!

P. J. O'ROURKE

B i d u k - b i d u k - b i d u k .
Phuttaphuttaphutta. Biduk-biduk-biduk.
Phuttaphuttaphutta. You know the fuck what that's the fucking sound of ? Fuck your ass, you do. Biduk-biduk-biduk. *Phuttaphuttaphutta.* Biduk-biduk-biduk. *Phuttaphuttaphutta.* Its the oh-so-clever smartass sound I make when I can't think of anything funny to write, *needledick.*

They say I'm the funniest writer in America. Not the funniest *waiter* or the funniest *whiter* — whatever that may be, screw you, fuckface — or the funniest *water* but the funniest writer! F-U-N-N-I-E-S-T W-R-I-T-E-R, goddit, noodlejerk? I was over in your rainsoaked dime of a country to prove it on your chat shows last fall and to say I had 'em howling would not, I repeat *not* be an insult to howling.

"You know what that Marilyn Quayle looks like?" I said on your *Wogan* show, all set to let the 9m audience into one of my best wet-your-pants jokes. "You know what Marilyn Quayle looks like?"

"Before you tell us, P.J.," Wogan butted in, "perhaps you'd better fill us in on who Marilyn Quayle is, exactly."

"Right, right," I said, stifling my chuckles, "Marilyn Quayle's the wife of Dan Quayle. And you know what she looks like, do you? Well, I'll tell you... "

"I'm sure we're all dyin' to be told," said Wogan, "but first, it might just be worth explaining to viewers who might not know, exactly who Dan Quayle is."

"Sure," I said — and by this time to say I was pissing my pants would be an insult to pant-pissers everywhere — "Dan Quayle is our Vice-President, and to say that he was thick would be an insult to... to... things that are thick. So, I'm telling you, Marilyn Quayle looks just like a... "

"So, to be sure, it's the Vice-President's wife we're talking about — I'm right there, am I?" said Wogan.

"Right. And in my book I say that she looks like a Water Buffalo!!!!!! In fact, to say she looks like a Water Buffalo would be an insult to Water Buffaloes!!!!!!"

"And tell us," smiled Wogan, "what does a Water Buffalo look like exactly?"

It's jokes like the Marilyn Quayle one — she looks like a Water Buffalo! — that have earned me the title of America's Funniest Humorist. But I'm not *just* a humorist. Oh, no, sirreee! To say that I'm just a humorist would not be not be so much not right as utterly wrong: R-O-N-G! I'm a chronicler of our times, using humour as a scalpel on society. Wasn't it Horace who said: "What stops a man who can laugh from speaking the truth?" Or was it "tooth"?!! And you're looking at that man now, baby. Lemme demonstrate what I mean by "Funniest Man in the Universe" by applying my technique to your own two-bit political set-up in England, home of the toffee-nose limey poofter, haven for the Ostentatiously Poor and the Social Security Trillionaire:

Neil Kinnock: As bald as the bass-drum at a Guns 'n' Roses gig, to say the guy's a windbag is an insult to windbags, goddammit!

John Major: What the fucking fuck the hell with goddamn asshole who gives a shit? Take dope? *You bet I do, crazy ass!* And I've scored some pretty nifty chicks in my time too, some of them with as much power in their thighs as a two thousand pound command-detonated motherfucker Scud missile launched on five thousand hankie-heads and sandmouths in Iraq. But what about this

John Major? He's as goddamn boring as queuing for tickets for a Madonna concert and then finally discovering when you reach the ticket box they've run out and she doesn't plan any more concerts for a year due to exhaustion, that's how boring John Major is.

SeewhaddImean? These aren't just ordinary jokes, they're jokes that *reveal the truth about those who would seek to govern us and about human life in general, the truth that all men and women in the USA are worthy of God's love and are thankful to live in the Land of the Free.* If this lone humorist has to shock, to outrage, to tear the whole goddamn place apart in some mad-dash-sweat-pounding-far-out-biduk-biduk-biduk-hyphenated-synonymic-scramble in order to proclaim the truth, then that's what he's gonna do, fatface. And no goddam nigger-loving hymie sauerkraut-eating bidet-slooshing bastard sonofabitch is gonna stop him.

Myself, I've been around, but I'll tell you this, and that's for free, sure it is, baby, and I'm not one to mess around, no way, but this I will tell you, once, twice, ten zillion times: I'll never forget — *never* — how to get away with spinning out a sentence — see it spin, daddio! — by placing more words in it than it deserves and thereby fooling airheads and napkinbrains into believing that it's not just *humorous* but *hipppppppp and reeeelly koooooollll!!*

Ethiopia, Schmethiopia, so they're poor and starving, huh? Biiiiiig deal. They're still not fashionable, not by any cast-iron American standards. No food? Know how they feel. Hell, I've waited over twenty-five minutes to get served at Sardi's, but I don't go whining about it to NBC and walking around in the sand with all my clothes off!!! What the fuck? Like, they're so thin they make Ivana Trump look like, look like, look like — yeah, look like she wasn't very thin! I took the airplane to Ethiopia, one famine before last. Let's just say it wasn't exactly Disneyworld!!! I mean, these guys didn't even speak *English*. No wonder they never got to get their main course — the waitress obviously didn't understand 'em!!! And those babies crying their little non-white heads off like Donald Duck just zapped his wonger in one of their moms! Give me Santa Monica any day, with a Pina Colada, a top-heavy chick, a club sandwich, some drugs — yeah, you could say I took drugs! — a nice clean white shirt and some red-hot American hi-guys-howyadoin *service*!

I suppose you could call me outrageous. That's what they've always called guys who've laughed in the face of untruth. But say what you like about America — and I'll admit we have our fair share of flag-desecrators, welfare-malingerers, wilfully one-legged, Johnny-No-Eyes, liberal-bedwetters, hairy-armed-feminist-lesbian-terrorists and crosspatch-rape-victims — there's really No Place Like Home. And to say that that's not an outrageous thought is, you might say, an insult to outrageous thoughts! So it's over and out from the funniest guy in the world! Biduk-biduk-biduk, *phuttaphuttaphutta*.

MICHAEL WINNER

 I am what someone once termed "a living legend". Anecdotes about That Man Winner, fond or otherwise, are rife in the world of movies, and my witticisms are rightly celebrated.

There was the famous time when a novice reporter asked me for my definition of teamwork. "A hundred different people all doing what I tell them," I replied, quick as a flash — an off-the-cuff remark that has now entered into history. And my definition of how to make a great movie? "A lot of different people — all doing what I tell them." That one, too, has made it into the textbooks. And a final Winnerism, as they're known within the industry: when asked by a fledgling journalist for his secret of success, Michael Winner retorted: "My secret of success? Getting everyone to do what I tell them!!"

 A s anyone who reads the national press will know, I am the proud possessor of an enchanting lady who goes by the name of Miss Jenny Seagrove — and what better present could any man have, I ask you, than to wake up beside that gorgeous and delectable lady?

As the lucky owner of the positively magical Miss Seagrove, I like to celebrate my admiration for this one hundred per cent female by purchasing imaginative gifts for her Birthday. Last year, the Band of the Royal Scots Guards played *Happy Birthday to You* while the two of us — myself and the lovely Miss Seagrove — enjoyed a Champagne Breakfast on the lawn. It was a purely personal way of rejoicing in our union, something private and very loving. Even the hard-nosed hacks from the *Mail*, *Sunday People*, *Mirror*, *Sun* and *Daily Express* whom I invited along to record the event agreed with me that this was a very special, very private tribute to a very luscious young lady.

 T his year, my plans are already far advanced for the most spectacular Birthday present yet. I am, as you will know, not just Britain's premier — some would say only — film director, but also the Founder and Chairman of the Police Memorial Trust, a Trust I initiated following the tragic murder of PC Yvonne Fletcher outside the Libyan Embassy, for which I have earned universal praise from all right-minded folk.

Well, this year I plan to transport Miss Seagrove in my chauffeur-driven limousine to St James's Square, there to hear Mr Nigel Kennedy, Miss Kiri Te Kanawa, the lovely "Bananarama" trio, Mr Val Doonican and the ladies and gents of the Hallé Orchestra play a selection from the Brahms *Requiem* on the very spot where that tragic young lady was so ruthlessly gunned down, while we both tuck into a Champagne Breakfast, still clad in our pyjamas and silk dressing gowns. A beautiful tribute to two beautiful young ladies.

 T hose who know me only as the highly successful director of the movie *Death Wish* (1974) would be well advised to check out my more artistic, impressionistic and delicately etched films, for which I have earned all the plaudits going from fair-minded critics such as my good friend Jeff Tingle, Chief Showbiz Reporter on the *News of the World*. These include *The Mechanic*

(1972), *Death Wish II* (1981), *The Stone Killer* (1973) and *Death Wish III* (1985). It gets up my nose no end that many of the more high-falutin' — and lowly paid, might I add — members of the British Press have, for reasons not unassociated with jealousy, chosen to ignore these considerable artistic achievements. Isn't it about time they banged the drum for Britain, I ask myself ? Well, even those notorious toffee-noses will be forced to pay tribute to my next two movies: Anita Brookner's quiet masterpiece *Hotel du Lac* and Kazuo Ishiguro's sensitive and haunting *The Remains of the Day*, Booker Prizewinners both.

Filming of *Hotel du Lac* starts in Geneva this spring, with that fine actress Miss Jenny Seagrove gracing the screen with her presence as spinster and novelist Euphemia Blissit looking back on her life, and Mr Charles Bronson as the ruthless assassin who will stop at nothing to blow her to bits with a Howitzer Pump-Action Shotgun. Then in the autumn we begin work on *The Remains of the Day*, with the part of the English butler coming to terms with the events of the past played by Miss Jenny Seagrove, and Mr Charles Bronson playing the ruthless assassin who will stop at nothing to strip her naked and humiliate her before blowing her brains out with a stolen Exocet missile. For once in their paltry lives, the so-called critics will be duty-bound to award Winner the artistic credit that has long been his due.

In my role as Founder and Chairman of the Police Memorial Trust, I have no little influence over those who rule our land. Mrs Thatcher — now there's a lady with guts — became a close personal friend when we appeared side by side together while Miss Sarah Brightman sang a selection from Lloyd-Webber at the unveiling of the memorial to WPC Yvonne Fletcher in St

James's Square five years ago. "How on earth did that awful little man take control?" I overheard her whisper to an adviser — a clear reference to Colonel Gadaffi. I then took the trouble to inform the good lady exactly how it is possible for a bloodthirsty madman with no talent to make his way in the world through sheer ruthless ambition and a love of guns. "At least you're honest about it," she replied enigmatically.

★ STAR THOUGHTS ★
ROBERT MAXWELL

The last couple of weeks have witnessed the brilliantly outstanding success of my latest venture, *The European.* I am delighted to announce that we sold out our first printing of over fifty-five million — that's one each for every man, woman and child in this country — and we were forced to print a second edition of four hundred million on hearing that the Chinese were clamouring for it too. These outstandingly excellent results were due in no small part to the fascinating polls we conducted among a sample of over fifty people in and beyond the Holborn area. In answer to the question: "Which leading public figure in the world do you feel is most deserving of an hereditary peerage?", we were frankly astonished to find that 99 per cent answered: "Robert Maxwell MC", while to the question: "Who would be the most suitable monarch for a united Europe?", the answers were a little more varied, with 15 per cent voting for Queen Elizabeth II, 3 per cent voting for King Juan Carlos of Spain and just 82 per cent voting for Robert Maxwell MC.

CLAIRE RAYNER

She'll be feeling a little bit lost, a little bit lonely, poor love, bless her. Not nice at all, that I've-just-lost-my-job feeling. After the initial emotions of freedom, those "last-week-I-was-Prime-Minister-this-week-I'm-a-great-big-nobody" feelings will be setting in. But it's something we all have to go through at one time or another. Hey ho. Frankly, Margaret, if you're reading this and you'd like to write to me personally, I'll answer in total confidence but do please remember to send a stamped addressed envelope, there's a love.

A few words of advice. Life's too short to mooch about feeling sorry for yourself, honestly it is love. Get stuck into a good book. Ring a friend — hang the expense, and cheaper rates are offered after six and at weekends. Take the dog for a walk. Get a really super new perm from your favourite hairdresser. Have a bit of a chinwag with a neighbour. Do something for someone else for a change. Lovely. But for heaven's sake don't sit around feeling sorry for yourself, that doesn't do anyone any good, honestly it doesn't. I've got a mountain of booklets and pamphlets offering helpful advice on the subject, Margaret, so do please write in and I'll be delighted to send them off.

Do's and Don'ts (No.1): Television is for watching, not for eating. I only wish more people would get this simple fact into their heads. Consuming a television might well be fun, but it's really not very wise. By all means eat some chocolates or even your tea while watching the old gogglebox — nothing wrong with that, do it myself, lovely — but please, please, PLEASE try to lay off the knobs and wires. Not only can it play havoc with your digestion; it ruins the picture for everyone else and can cause terrible problems within the family unit.

Went to a super play called *Hamlet* last week. Super, but silly. Frankly I can't be doing with people who get themselves all worked up into an awful tizz about nothing. If the poor fella had asked my advice, I'd have told him in no uncertain terms:

a) In my dictionary, there's no such word as can't.

b) For heaven's sake, let's not cry over spilt milk.

c) Cheer up — it might never happen!

But would he have listened? Would he heck! A very wise and lovely man, real gem, once told me: "Some people never learn." Bend back that lughole, Hamlet, bless you, and try listening to other people for a change, there's a love.

Do's and Don'ts (No.2): Whatever you do, I beg, beg, BEG of you not to put your hand in a raging fire. It'll hurt dreadfully, and you won't feel any the better for it. Instead, why not put your hand in a pocket, and put logs on the fire? It's a trick that's worked for a lot of super people, and there's no reason why it shouldn't work for you. Logs or coal, yes: hands and feet no — that's the Rayner Way when it comes to fires.

A lot of problems to get through, so quick, quick, quick.

Cecil from Hertford: You got your secretary in the family way, your wife stood by you, you made a comeback, couldn't manage, your boss was ditched and now you're out too. Secretary stroppy, wife moody, boss miserable, Cecil down in the dumps. My advice? Cheer up, Cecil — the rest of us are laughing fit to bust. **Carol from Dulwich**: You tell me that since your mummy's left her post, no one seems to want to employ you. My advice? Why not try a change of job? At the moment you are struggling to be a writer, but why not switch to something more suited to your obvious talents? Have you ever thought of being a bollard? I noticed one missing on the A24 intersection the other day. It could be just the ticket. **Norma from Huntingdon**: Don't let them get at you, love. We can't all have a full wardrobe and if *you* think you look nice in that blue suit, well, that's half the battle won. Life's too short to be worrying about appearances, believe you me. Do let us know how you get on.

*D*o's and Don'ts (No.3): Trouser pockets can be an awful hazard around the home. If I've said it once, I've said it a thousand times: do, I beg of you, make sure that your pockets aren't drenched full of petrol before putting your trousers or slacks on in the morning. It only takes one match to light and — whoosh! — the next thing you know you're faced with a desperately sad family bereavement, and the additional financial burden of a new pair of trousers, should the poor love survive.

M y readers, bless 'em, tell me that I'm a super, caring sort of person, someone with a shoulder to cry on. I'm always ready with advice and I guess that's why I'm such a busy little bee! "Dear Claire," one of my fans wrote only the other day, "I've murdered my husband and children and the house is being repossessed. I'm dying of terminal cancer and the washing-machine's broken down. I've just lost my job, and my parents have just died in a car-crash, I don't have any friends and there's only John Major on television. Please advise."

"Take a deep breath," I replied. "Make yourself a nice hot cuppa and put your feet up. There. Feel better already, I bet. Now. Let your fingers do the walking through your local Yellow Pages. 'P' for Plumber is what you are after. Found it? Right. Give him a tinkle, he's probably a super fella, and he'll be round in a jiffy to mend that old wagger-magger of yours. As to the other problems, well, frankly love, time's a terrific healer."

*D*o's and Don'ts (No.4): I'll tell you something that gets right up my nose. People who think that they can put their head under water for over half an hour and still come up breathing. If I've said it once I've said it a hundred times but I don't mind if I go on saying it till I'm blue in the face: the longer you put your head under water, the more likely you are to drown. My advice? The next time you see water, whether in a pond or in the sea or even at home in your own basin, do try to avoid putting your head in it for more than a couple of minutes. It'll save you and your family a helluva lot of trouble, lovey.

KINGSLEY AMIS

What a bloody hopeless lot most modern thingies are. Writers. Modern writers. That's it. What a bloody hopeless lot most thingy writers are. Can't form a grammatical sentence for one thing and for another they sort of let their so-called lucid prose (i.e. self-regarding rubbish) spread out all over the shop, never knowing when to come to the end and instead dragging on so long that by the time you manage to get to the end you forget what it was they were going on about at the beginning and it probably wasn't worth the effort anywayish sort of thing.

I'll tell you what and that's this. What they need is a lesson in how to write. They should be like what I am. I take care to listen for the *nuances* (bloody typical writerish word *that*) of everyday speech. "Gor Blimey, Guv," a cab-driver said to me a week or so ago, "any old iron, me hearty." As soon as I got back to my desk, I wrote it down after having a bottle of Scotch or so, and now I daresay it'll pop up in my next novel, along with "Cheers, mate" and "It's a fair cop", both of them very up-to-the-minute expressions in contemporary (i.e. bloody awful) society. No wonder they call me the master of everyday thingy.

I took my son Martin to lunch at The Garrick the other day. Spewed everywhere, and kept asking the Head Waiter if he had a spare condom, used or unused, he wasn't fussy. Martin parades an interest in the raw underside of life (i.e. smut) and it's impossible to take him bloody anywhere. Before I'd even got my bib into my collar, he'd started picking his left nostril with the Garrick Club serving spoon, and by the time the beef and Yorkshire pud arrived he was going hammer and tongs at his thingy under the cloth. Perry Worsthorne arrived at our table just as the lad was experiencing a certain amount of disorder in the phlegm department. "Paradoxically..." began Perry, but his freshly-minted aphorism was alas cut short by a shower of ear-wax extracted from the ear of Amis Junior by imaginative employment of the Club cigar-cutter. It found its final resting-place in the centre of Perry's pristine silk tie. As we were all perusing the globule, Lord Denning sidled up, took one look at Perry's new emblem and congratulated him on his election to the MCC. All very chummy, or it would have been had not Martin chosen that moment to take a bite at his toe-nails, the clippings leaping hugger-mugger into the horse-radish. If you think his "novels" are disgusting, you should see the state of his socks.

And another thing wrong with modern life. Have you noticed how the telephone always has to "ring" before you can pick it up to speak to the person at the other end? Yet another example of the shoddy lot in charge of the phones wanting to make life as noisy as bleeding possible, sod the public, that's you and me, the poor bloody heterosexual tax-payers, or at least me, I don't know what you are and I don't bloody care. And another thing. Why are modern showers designed so that you have to take your clothes off before getting into them? If you set the water going and then step in with your clothes still on, you get soaking bloody wet, but no one in their right mind (a minority, granted) wants to go to the bother of stripping naked just so's they can have a flipping shower. And whatever happened to Father Christmas, may I ask? There was a time when he provided a halfway-efficient service, entering with a stocking as near as dammit to midnight on Christmas Eve but I haven't heard from the old bugger now for sixty-odd years. Probably joined a Lesbian Architectural Co-Operative, no doubt on an Arts Council Grant, so now he can just sit around "creating" rather than doing what he's employed to do, i.e. give me my stocking. Christmas isn't what it was, but then what is?

And another thing. I found myself in the National Gallery the other day. It's in the same area as The Garrick and their front doors are just about identical. Searching about for the bloody bar, I asked for a gin-and-vodka from a woman (of course) only to be told that she served postcards, diaries, calendars and souvenir novelty items of an arty sort and if I wanted a drink I should clear bloody off. On the way out, I caught sight of a painting described in sod-you small type underneath as *The Nativity*. Repulsive little fat family, he bearded and with a don't-blame-me expression on his face, she with a look of contentment as if to say ha bloody ha now you'll have to cough up for maintenance, and the titchy blighter smiling a sod-you-matey smile, and all taking place in some sort of makeshift barn or "chalet" as it was no doubt advertised. What I want to know is why can't painters paint paintings which the rest of us can sort of enjoy? Why not a few at-least-semi-skilled pictures of taxpaying heterosexual male carnivores sitting in an orderly fashion exchanging right-minded opinions over a Scotch-and-Rum rather than all this stuff showing foreign one-parent families struggling in "underprivileged" (my foot) conditions?

My next novel, *Same Again Please,* is about a bloke who has all sorts of females and assorted misfits on his back but sometimes manages to nip down the pub to talk to other blokes about how awful the females etcetera are and at some point a cabbie comes and takes him to and fro saying "Cheers" and "Pardon me may I use your toilet, guv?" and in the end everything remains more or less the same only his ex-wife Loopy, who's now married to Geoffrey's ex-wife Mania's sort of nephew, Chris, decides to run off with Chris's lesbian flatmate Schizo, who was once kind of engaged to Loopy's ex-neighbour's ex-husband's sort of brother-in-law Patrick, the librarian, but this doesn't really affect the main character much as far as one can tell, though he can't for the life of him remember who Geoffrey was in the first place. Should be a lot better than anything by those "modernist" (pull the other) American "creative" novelists who only write about their own little corners of the globe, lazy sods.

ESTHER RANTZEN CBE

Busy, busy, busy. I'm always in a rush, rather like Mr Tony RUSH, a personnel manager from Brentford, who, frankly, must be RUSHed off his feet! And his wife, Mrs Margaret RUSH probably never draws breath, she's in so much of a RUSH! And as for their children, Jack and Hayley RUSH, they must both be in quite a little RUSH too (groan!).

As you may have gathered by now, you have to have a highly-developed sense of humour in a job like mine. My diary is full all this year, and I have just inked in my last available date in December. The Dean of St Paul's has written a very kind letter asking if myself and my husband, Desmond, and our children Esther (11) and Des (9) will pose in a *tableau vivant* for their Christmas crib. It's a great honour, and I feel very humbled to be playing the part of the Virgin Mary, with my daughter as the Infant Jesus, my son as Joseph and my husband Desmond as either a donkey or a mangy old piece of straw. If it does anything to make the Christmas message — an end to all child abuse — more relevant, then it must be a good thing.

It makes me feel very humble to think that we are the nation's choice as the Holy Family. We'll do the job as well as we humanly can. One small point: if only the *That's Life* team (and we

ARE a team, let's not forget) had been around in Bethlehem, we'd have been down on that innkeeper like a ton of bricks.

Names that make you chuckle (1): I note that a bank-manager from Epping I have just made up is called "MR TOILET-PAPER". Worth approaching for a wee, wee loan, maybe?!!

We've been getting a lot of complaints recently from viewers who have bought themselves trouser-belts from leading high-street retailers. "I pulled my belt too tight," writes a typical viewer, Mr P. Randall from Uxbridge. "And I found that my waist was painful all day."

The same happened to Mr Trevor Johns from Croydon, who pulled his belt a full *two notches* too tight. "I was in no mood to let the matter rest," Mr Johns told us. "So I took my complaint direct to the manufacturer. Eventually, I got a letter back saying that the fault was MINE and that I shouldn't have pulled it so tight in the first place!!"

Well, we thought we'd take this scandal further, and we rang a Mr Stephens of The High Wycombe Belt Company in High Wycombe. "We've been getting a number of complaints about your belts," we said.

"Oh yes?" he said.

"OH YES!" we said. "A lot of our viewers have found that if they tie them too tight, they spend the rest of the day in some pain."

We must admit to being absolutely stunned by the reply Mr Stephens then gave us.

"They've only got themselves to blame," he said.

"But why have you not fitted SAFETY LOCKS to your belts, to stop people pulling them too tight and hurt-

ing themselves?" we asked. Eventually, Mr Stephens said he would *"look into the matter"*.

We wonder just how many people will have to walk around with painful waists before LEGISLATION is brought in to guard against belts that can be pulled too tight. Until that day, we have set up a special BELTWATCH number — 031-6591-3947 — for you to ring, day or night, if you feel that your belt has been pulled too tight. So far, there have been no deaths from overtight belts, but we fear that a tragedy can't be too far off. If you hear of such an awful tragedy, do let us know, and we'll do our best to feature it on a forthcoming show, perhaps with a song-and-dance routine from our very own Doc Cox.

It has come to my notice in recent months that a great many very sick people — there's no other word for them — are biting the heads off goldfish. Though we haven't yet heard of a single instance of this growing epidemic that is sweeping the country, we know that the vast majority of the great British public will wish to help us stamp it out. We have plans afoot to place adhesive tape around the necks of all goldfish registered in this country so as to deter these evil people. Until then, if you SEE a goldfish with its head bitten off, or if indeed you ARE a goldfish with its head bitten off, please, please, *please* give us a call on our special GOLDFISHWATCH day and night service. You can choose whether you would prefer to speak to a trained doctor or direct to a goldfish, and your call will be taken in total confidence.

Names that make you chuckle (2): I couldn't help but notice that the man who elected to share his marital bed with yours truly rejoices in the surname of "WILL-COCK". Here's hoping that Where there's a WILL, there's a COCK!

These days, it seems as if the whole country is talking about just one thing: who will be the lucky winner of our auditions to find a new *That's Life* presenter? We've been frankly dumbfounded by the great mass of sheer talent out there. Thirty of you, for instance, came up with really first-class impersonations of Frank Spencer saying "Ooooh, Betty!", and there were no less than fifty-eight applicants who were able to touch the tips of their noses with their tongues!

What a brilliant lot of people you are! From this wealth of talent, it's our job to choose a new presenter — no easy task! So far, we've whittled the original number down, first to fifteen, and then to ten, as one or two pulled out when they heard that the job of presenting *That's Life* is not all fun and skittles. Before any new *That's Life* presenter reaches your screens, he has undergone not only one helluva lot of sheer hard work but also a full castration under medical supervision. Some of them just weren't up to making this sacrifice, so, regrettably, we had to wish them the best of luck elsewhere. The others now are in full possession of the necessary high voices, uncertain smiles and what we call "deference to Esther" that is required from a *That's Life* presenter, and in future weeks we'll be awarding their penises mounted on plaques to the viewers who come up with the sausage or frankfurter which looks most like a *That's Life* presenter's PRIVATE PART!! Happy hunting!

THE RT HON EDWARD HEATH MP

Might I make one thing quite clear from the outset. I hold no relish for the situation into which my party has found itself enmeshed these past sixteen years. I do not gloat. Far from it. Absolutely not. Nothing could be further from the truth. Nor do I rejoice in the pitiful — and, to her former colleagues, painfully embarrassing — state to which the previous Prime Minister, a Mrs Margaret Thatcher, has been reduced. When I heard the news of her resignation following the resounding humiliation meted out to her in the first ballot, I did not rejoice. This was no time for jubilation. One does not delight in the misfortune of others. One looks to the long-term future of this country and its role in Europe, of course one does.

The night of the woman's resignation, I sat by myself contemplating the long-term future of the country and its role in Europe with a decent spread of gulls' eggs and vol-au-vents and some very acceptable Pol Roger champagne. As a small danceband struck up a few "up-tempo" tunes in the corner of my drawing room I found myself tapping my feet. But let me add this. It pained me to witness scenes of Mrs Margaret Thatcher's obvious distress, visible disappointment and crushing humiliation on the 6 O'Clock News, the 7 O'Clock News, the 9 O'Clock News, the 10 O'Clock News and on *Newsnight*, and all over again a couple of times on video. Though my neighbours may well have heard great bellows of laughter emerging from my chambers, these were only intermittent and my deepest sympathies remained with her. I would not know, but I imagine it cannot be remotely amusing to realise the country has decided that enough is enough and they had had just about as much as they can stand of your shrill, womanly bossiness. She never concealed her jealousy of me and my rapport with the people, but I am now more than happy to wish her a very long retirement.

Historians will judge that it was my famous laugh that has endeared me for so long to the British people. I am, I suppose, something of a father-figure to the nation. Talking, as I often have cause to, to what one might term the "real" people — butlers, servants, chauffeurs, doormen, that sort of thing — one is constantly struck by the genuine affection in which one continues to be held. "Thank you, Sir, thank you very much," a cloakroom attendant at the Savoy Hotel said to me the other day as I placed a twenty-pence piece in his tray. I receive similar compliments all the time from people the length of the country. Many of them, I imagine, have great hopes that I shall shortly be returning to my home at Number 10. To them I say this. The present incumbent, a Mr Major, may not be a man of very great weight or stature. Indeed, some would argue that he is an out-and-out nonentity. But he is doing his modest best, and he has already sought my advice on a number of important issues. Give him time, and if, as I feel sadly confident, he fails to win the next election, the party will doubtless come cap in hand to their one elder statesman of international repute. Might I add that, in the event, I will unify the party by offering Mrs Margaret Thatcher a post in Government. Her proven ability would make her, to my mind, an ideal secretary for one of our many prestigious Commons sub-committees.

An amusing story that may well raise a chuckle among the more humorously inclined. Mrs Margaret Thatcher recently fell over and hurt her knee badly, putting her out of action for several days. Like all the best stories, it's perfectly true, and somehow appropriate. Anyway, it made me laugh.

As expected, I came in for a fair amount of carefully orchestrated criticism when I suggested we could never win a war in the Gulf and that it would end in nuclear conflagration. Yet, once again, events have proved me absolutely right. At the time, I was privileged to be granted an audience with President Hussein of Iraq. I found him to be an international statesman of considerable acumen, possessing a deep love of classical music and a broad interest in the future of Europe. We discussed wide-ranging issues for three hours seated upon the very finest 18th-century French furniture, with a splendid tea laid on at his own expense. The carpeting was excellent throughout, and his taste in silver and cutlery is impeccable. Throughout, he treated me with all the honour due a leading figure in world affairs. Yet still the man is portrayed as some sort of ogre. Is this really the way to treat a politician of undoubted ability? "I trust that this will do something to redress the balance," I told him before my departure, handing him a signed copy of my bestselling book, *Sailing* (1975) and two tickets for a concert conducted by my-

self featuring the Portsmouth Sinfonia in the Birmingham Gaumont next autumn (seats still available at all prices). "I will read this with great interest," he said. Incidentally, it may interest those who speak of Saddam's so-called "cruelty" to know that he has since ordered no less than two thousand copies of *Sailing* and another two thousand of *Music* (1976) to be read aloud to his most distinguished political prisoners, day and night. The results, he tells me, have already proved "most satisfactory".

Whilst my ill-fated successor as Leader of the Conservative Party was never able to command the affection of the Commons tea-room — far from it, I'm afraid — I am well-liked and admired by a broad range of my colleagues in Parliament. My successor was never good at small talk, you see — I suppose it had something to do with the fact that she was quite obviously not a man's man — whereas I could talk on equal terms even to the very footling little people of no significance whatsoever. I remember, for instance, back in 1976 casually walking up and saying: "That's my chair you're sitting on," to a very junior backbencher. It was a comment that broke the ice, and he immediately stood up and handed the chair over to me. Again, I always make a point of acknowledging the greetings of my fellow MPs. The last time it happened, back in 1973, a young fellow said: "Good morning, Mr Heath," to which I replied, "Who are you?" He went to great lengths to explain that he had been my Private Secretary for the past two years. "I see," I replied. Such warm, very personal contact is vital if one is to carry the party with one, a lesson my successor would have done well to learn, poor dear!!!

NICHOLSON BAKER

My beard contains a certain tangled *moistiness*, the dewy, drip-dropping, effluvescent, rain-forestishy dampness you sometimes find in lavatories when you place your hand in the bowl and refulgently swish it around, the exact same notion (though slightly different) that, as a child, I employed when mulishly tugging at a kite to stop it from falling parenthetically to the ground, leading me to ask the question why my beard (formed from hundreds and hundreds of hairs growing on my face, each peeping its dark and pin-y head a further three millimetres out into the open air each day, all the time contributing in some symbiotic and unknowingly *communal* way to a rich down of wirey undergrowthishness) should be so *moist* (a word I have noted used to great and giddying effect in Nabokov's *Pale Face* (Nabokov is really simply *super*, really amazingly *super*) (and also in Updike, though I forget the exact reference now (actually it was at the bottom of page 97 of one of his books, but I forget which, just as I have forgotten why I started this sentence about my beard))).

On the 15th July 1989 at 4.35 pm I was reading a review of a book of reviews, one of which was a review of a new book of reviews in which the reviewer was praising a new book of reviews by a leading reviewer, I forget just who (and regrettably I can't check it out because I've told myself that if I check it out then the 1992 Pulitzer Prize for Fiction will not be mine, not that I'm saying that I deserve it, just that if I *did* deserve it, which I don't, then I might

not get it if I checked out the reviewer whose name I've forgotten. Actually, I remember his name now, but he's not particularly well known so I won't bother to mention it). In this review, the reviewer quoted a piece from another review, this time by Saul Bellow (wow! Bellow's a beautiful, *beautiful* writer) and in the middle of this extract I spotted a semi-colon —

";"

sitting there, its nervy, circular, footballish, pinheady full stop, perfectly round like our very planety planet seen from space or like the interior of a drinking straw seen from above, balancing precariously on the eerily flexed arm of the supporting comma (gorgeously appropriate image) and something told me that Bellow (a disturbingly misnomonic surname, as in his rare public performances he tends to utter quietly, almost in a whisper (*whisper* — what a crisply evocative word)) had caught sight of one of my own semi-colons, perhaps in an article I had written for the *New Yorker* (me? write for the *New Yorker*? yes! it's true!) and had said to himself, "Hmmm, that talented young Nick Baker has employed a touching and affirmatively noble semi-colon in that sparkling prose of his — I think I will borrow it, as a small tribute to that exceedingly bright and luminously self-effacing young man." So there it was —

";"

my semi-colon, hand-picked by one of the great masters of the modern novel. But how was I to thank him for this detumescently incantatory tribute to one who was not fit to tie his shoe-laces, or at least how could I do it without simultaneously appearing to make it plain that I was perversely peeved by his "borrowing" of my punctuation? The writer's life is wrought with such conumbra.

"Dear Saul," I wrote. "I'm not even saying that you know who I am and there is no particular reason why, even if you do know who I am, you should have been a secret and fervent admirer of my work, ever since the publication of my first book in 1986. You don't need a philistine schmuck like me to tell you how good you are — I masturbate on a regular basis to your description of a blade of grass in *Henderson the Rain King*, so much so that my own very private name for the book is *Henderson the Wan King* — but I would like to point out that the semi-colon —

';'

— I saw quoted in a recent review seemed unnervingly — flatteringly — similar to the semi-colon —

';'

— I, Nick Baker (that's me: the Nick is short for Nicholson, and my surname is Baker: Nicholson Baker — it has a nice metaphonic ring to it don't you think?) employed halfway down page 25 of my seminal work, *NOB*, and I just want to assure you that I take this small act of plagiarism as a tribute, and that I know full well that without your superbly superb and complexly simple works of literature my own much smaller *oeuvre* would be less effective than your own. Do get in touch if you want help over future punctuation, yours prostrate, Nicholson Baker.

"PS. Please would you like my autograph?"

I have never successfully masturbated to Hugh Trevor Roper's writing, though I have to certain remembered scenes in J.K.P. Galbraith, and I find any dust-jacket photograph of William Golding powerfully erotic. Among English authors, I have masturbated successfully to the weekend essays of Roy Hattersley and some of the novels of Margaret Drabble, though Michael Holroyd's two-volume *Life of Shaw* seems to me just too *long* for sustained masturbation, and the bibliography at the end of Vol. 2 is a dampener equal to the appendix of Leon Edel's very Edelian *Life of Henry James*.

Searching for an idea for my new novel, I encircle the thin tubularishly plasticy knob at the top of the television set with my thumb and index finger and, pressing as if at my own erect member and simultaneously turning it less than forty-three degrees in an Easterly direction, I discover that the television has come alive with a rapidly-changing miscellany of words and pictures of haphazardly refulgent matters over which I have no control, or, as my father would say, in his style both cheerily direct and obstinately easy, I switch on the TV.

For one and a half seconds, I stare at a war barkingly fought, a bomb insistently exploding, a village weight-losingly starving, tanks rolling stubbornly along like mobile wheeled buttocks and I grow twitchy and fidgetyish. Re-focusing my field of vision, I note with ever-less-muted joy that I can see the reflection of my own face — the familiarly bristled beard, the satisfyingly symmetric orbs of the spectacles, one lens over each all-seeing eye — in the outer protective screen. Happy chance! The reflection offers peak viewing of a fresh and zealously-oiled zit that has appeared just above my right nostril. Against a fetchingly apt backdrop of war, I pierce my zit with the outer perimeter of my right thumbnail, creating a detumescent lake of zittishly opulent fluidy detritus, a personalised microcosm of the great, tragic lake in, I think, Pasternak's *Dr Zhivago*. I have it! *Zit*: A Novel About Facial Blemishes. I call my publishers. They go *wild*.

PETER MAYLE

I opened the door in my old, stone *Provence* home to find a marvellous *character très Français* standing there before me. With his long, ginger beard, his sunlit, cheeky eyes, a dirty, old Gitanes poking from his rustic, asparagus-filled mouth, and two, spare adjectives rustling in his grubby, voluminous pockets, I knew at once who he was. He was a magnificent old *Provençale* peasant I had just made up, and he seemed very happy to see me.

"*Bonjour, Monsieur Peter,*" he croaked, the string of onions swinging to and fro from his beret, occasionally knocking the bottle of Pernod from his *main.*

"*Bonjour*, amusing French character," I said. He grinned a toothless grin. Here in *Provence*, they simply adore being addressed on equal terms by retired executives with jocular spectacles. "And what have *vous* brought for me *aujourd'hui?*"

He reached deep into his hunting sack and pulled out what looked like a dirty old sock. Over a glass of wine (or two!) I asked him what it was. "It is what we *en Provence* call 'a dirty old sock', *Monsieur,*" he beamed, good-naturedly.

"And what, may I ask," I said, the clear, *Provençale* sunlight playing off the oil on my aubergine, "am I to do with it, *mon ami?*"

"Why, *monsieur,*" replied the gorgeous old character with a canny, endearing grin, "make a chapter out of it for *votre* latest book!"

Generously, I leant forward and poured him another half-glass of the local tapwater. I then sat down to write of the curious, amusing time when a delightful old character appeared at the door with an old sock in his sack. And to think they said nothing ever happened *ici!*

There are many old, wise sayings handed down from one generation of walnut-skinned rogues to the next. After a time spent in their company, gaining their trust, affection and admiration, I have been able to cull much wisdom from these horny-handed old timers. One of them opened the letter-hatch of our marvellous old front-door last week, and shouted through it, "You know, Peter, we have an old saying — 'Books sell best in the Autumn, but get more coverage in the Spring.' It was Monsieur Jeff from my publishers in London, alive, as always, to the ebb and flow of the rhythms of the seasons. I introduced him to Marcel and Georges, my trusty builders. "*Piss off,*" they replied, their English improving in leaps and bounds.

We have always found the everyday curiosities of French rural life amusing and interesting. From their smallest gestures, we realise that we have been accepted by the local community on our own terms. Everywhere we go — whether it is to buy *du pain* from *la boucherie* or to eat *boeuf en croûte* at the local *pharmacie* — they signal to us their pleasure in our company. They do this not with words, nor even with smiles, but with a single loving gesture. Placing their forefingers in the air and clenching their fists, they move their hands up and down in a swift, jerky rhythm. And, I might add, their sincerity cannot be doubted, for I have often caught sight of them performing this delightful ceremony, even while our backs are turned.

The *Provençale* is a simple yet complicated person, sometimes very tall yet often very small, with a great many of them fairly normal in stature. He likes to chat, yet he is also at times strangely silent. He is a creature of the outdoors, but often takes shelter in the home. He has a love of the sun, but has been known to be more than grateful for a drop of rain. He is an unabashed family man, yet he can sometimes be seen quite alone. A study of this often incorrigible, sometimes exasperating, always lovable creature would, I suspect, take a lifetime, yet how much more fascinating it is to nuzzle up to one *Provençal* builder caked in sweat, than to endure the boorishness, tedium and sheer vulgarity of the old friends one left behind!

Monsieur Bogusse arrived on our doorstep the other day. No one could be more typical than he. He speaks that special type of French so characteristic of the natives in my books: for much of the time he speaks in perfect English, but every now and then he reminds you that he is *Provençal* by inserting a *"celui-ci"* or an *"oh, là là"*.

Monsieur Bogusse has a larged waxed moustache of which he is inordinately proud. He wears a beret and a blue-and-white striped jersey, smells of garlic, rides a bicycle very dangerously, carries a French loaf behind each ear and whistles *La Marseillaise* as he gesticulates from behind a glass of rough peasant wine. In my book, he is as real as they come.

"Bonjour, Monsieur Bogusse!" I exclaimed. "And what brings you *ici*, this cheery May morn?"

"Monsieur Mayle," he said, "you are a — 'ow you say? — *smugtwat.*"

"Merci, Monsieur Bogusse," I replied, promising myself to look up that puzzler *smugtwat* in my invaluable French/English dictionary. But I have learnt in Provence that there is a language beyond words, and I could tell from his look that, as a representative of the local community, he was bestowing upon me the highest form of Gallic praise.

"And I want your *argent*," he said, a broad smile darkening his rugged features.

Around this time of year, ancient *Provençal* tradition dictates that one or more chaps from the local community get together to visit the foreigner's beautiful old home. Then, with hand outstretched, they request cash, folklore suggesting that this will ensure the survival of the beautiful old home throughout the coming four seasons. Happily entering into the spirit of this delicious old tradition, I handed over my wallet. In return, I received the customary trophy of a marvellous piece of *le gob* jettisoned from the mouth of Monsieur Bogusse with native accuracy straight onto the toe of my Clark's Leisurewear Sunsoak Sandal.

Looking down, I noted with excitement that the shape, colour and texture of *le gob* were just like the truffle soaked in oil and green pepper I had enjoyed the day before at *Le Petit Bistro Solange* run by the estimable Madame Valerie. It was then that I remembered that Monsieur Bogusse was her Head Chef. Ah, *le cuisine de la campagne! Toujours, Provence*, I thought to myself, and, even more super from all my readers' point of view, *Toujours Peter Mayle.*

THE RT HON ROY HATTERSLEY MP

I have no doubt that it will be observed by lesser mortals that, in penning this diary for a journal with which my disagreements are both profound and far-reaching, I have, in a sense, earned the none-too-illustrious mantle of game-keeper turned poacher, or vice-versa, depending upon where your own particular sympathies may, or may not, be inclined to lie at any one particular moment.

But I have always maintained that it is efficacious to bear in mind the old Yorkshire adage of my youth: "If you can't beat 'em, join 'em." I need hardly add, however, that, while I am widely regarded as a politician of no little seriousness who neither fair wind nor foul will budge one jot from his profoundly held beliefs, as a master of the pen, nib, and ink I am blessed with what might be called, in the words of the sage, "a lighter touch", as able to turn my immensely good-humoured gaze to, say, an essay In Praise of the Pork Chop as to a more considered analysis of the very real dilemmas facing my friends in the Muslim community. For the former type of literary ramble, this reprehensible journal might not seem such a disreputable stamping-ground, so, as the good burghers of Barnsley are wont to intone, "'ere we go!"

Charity obliges me to pass lightly over the fact that the very magazine which is now to help placate my ever-patient bank manager by an all-too-modest contribution to my paltry coffers is the very same journal which has found cause to poke a malicious and frankly bullying finger in the direction of my eating habits. So let's settle this matter once and for all. The sum total of my food consumption for an average day is as modest as it is nutritious. Breakfast, that most agreeable of meals, consists of a glass of orange juice, two pieces of lightly-buttered toast and a cup of freshly-brewed coffee, hardly a headline story, even to one of Mr Murdoch's scrupulously objective lackeys. Elevenses consists of two fried eggs, a couple of sausages, bacon, a single slice of fried bread and another cup of freshly-brewed coffee. Again, not much to write home about there. I have always maintained a firm rule that I should never consume more than two main courses at luncheon, and I defy anyone to produce evidence that this is a rule I have ever partaken to break. I have a weakness, I admit, for a creamy pudding, but even my dearest friends have never seen me get through any more than three at one sitting, with coffee and perhaps a choccie or two to follow, Rowntree's for preference.

I have often been known to leave out an early-to-mid afternoon snack altogether, though for health reasons I try not to miss a decent afternoon tea, but with a strict limit to scones (3), fancy-cakes (2) and — a Yorkshire favourite — flapjacks (4), all washed down with a good, hot, strong cup of tea, purchased from my friends in the Muslim community.

If the House is sitting, I tend to smuggle a smidgin of High Tea — perhaps a toasted cheese and baked bean sandwich, or some of Mr Matthews's excellent Turkey Drumsticks — into the Chamber in a trouser pocket, to be consumed under the cloak of a working brief. I eschew entirely any temptation towards a pre-dinner snack, though I might have a pack or two of pork scratchings, a much-underrated comestible in my humble opinion. And so to the main meal of the day, namely supper, where I allow myself meat and two veg, no more and no less. If I am working late, this will be followed by a working dinner of, say, scrambled eggs and mushy peas while watching *Newsnight*, that most informative of current affairs programmes, and so to bed, cocoa in hand, ready for ups when the alarm goes for a midnight Jaffa Cake. I hope this has done something to eradicate the notion of the present writer as some sort of gourmand or glutton that seems to be held in some none-too-lofty circles. It quite simply will not wash, as anyone with the full complement of eyes may now feel inclined to admit.

Laying that old bugbear to rest has all but cost me my allotted verbiage, so I would like to end, as any maestro of the old-fashioned manual typewriter must aim so to do, on something of a lighter note. Those esteemed readers who have persevered with me through the vicissitudes of my various jottings in the *Listener*, the *Guardian* and the late, lamented *Punch* will know by now that I am something of a dab hand at taking myself none-too-seriously. In fact, I have long regarded it as the hallmark of any fully paid up member of the human race that he should be able to laugh at himself on a regular basis. What follows, then, is a joke at my own expense.

"Mr Hattersley, sir," one of my friends from the Muslim community said last week, touching my coat. "You are being a great man, sir."

"Nonsense!" I replied. "I might forgive your grammatical inaccuracies if I were more fully convinced of the real truth behind your verbal felicities." Needless to say, your humble scribe led the laughter.

★ STAR THOUGHTS ★
DR DAVID OWEN

Some ordinary people tell me that they have not seen me on television for a while. Not so, in fact quite the opposite, absolutely and without a shadow of a doubt. The truth of the matter is that I have been offered a lucrative deal by the powers-that-be on *Jackanory*, the influential young persons' television programme, and I have more than once appeared on *Points West*, the important magazine programme for the South West, for which I am also booked later this month for their pioneering "Where Are They Now?" slot. If this is what they call "not being on television", then I am not Prime Minister! Incidentally, since some of the less important TV shows — the News and suchlike — have shown less specific interest in me as of late (long ago I advised them that it was time to give Bush, Gorbachev and the Pope a turn) I have formulated my own SDP Satellite Television station, to keep all SDP members and their friends up-to-date with our very latest policy formulations, cabinet appointments, etcetera. This important new station is based in the main sitting-room of my house in Limehouse, East London, and it's designed to work independent of electricity or satellites or other often-faulty new technology. The SDP and our friends all gather in the sitting room, Rosie and Mr Rosie on one sofa, the one with glasses and his wife on the other sofa, Debbie and the children on the floor, and me kneeling down behind a television that has been specially hollowed-out for the purpose. This way, I can keep everyone in touch with my latest views on Gorbachev's next step, a solution to the Iran/Iraq war, the future of the EMS and every other vital issue of the day.

HAROLD PINTER

Happy Christmas, they say. Not just Christmas. Oh, no. Not just Christmas. But *Happy* Christmas. Sometimes the hypocrisy of these people is so sickening it makes me want to vomit.

Let me explain as best I can using words. My wife Lady Antonia and I were in a large department store in that area of London between South Kensington and Piccadilly. We were considering the purchase of Christmas gifts for an acquaintance of ours aged within the region of six years old. After some thought, I had in mind something black. But I did not know what.

"Black," I said to the woman in her forties behind the counter. "I want something black."

"Black?" she said.

"Yes," I said. "Something black. I want something black. Something black is what I want. What I want is something black."

"This is the toy department," she countered. "There's not much black here. A police car, I suppose."

"A police car?" I said to the woman in her forties. "A pig car? I suppose you want me to buy torturing irons as well? And electric shock equipment? And a gun to shoot down innocent men? Is that it? IS THAT IT? Come on, Lady Antonia, we're not staying to hear any more of this crap, get your coat. I've never been so offended in my life."

We exited that minute, Antonia stopping certainly no more than three minutes to order a couple of new corner-cushions from the soft furnishings department and then we stormed out in disgust. "I agree with you, Harold," agreed Antonia. "And I'm certainly never shopping *here* again except on Tuesdays and Fridays."

We bought our acquaintance aged within the region of six years something more suitable elsewhere. A pair of dark glasses and a Christmas card, also in black. I wrote inside: "Wishing you a not too unhappy Christmas, the present Tory Junta permitting." In case he felt like celebrating, I enclosed a paper hat, also in black.

For Christmas lunch this year, we plan to commemorate the atrocities committed during the Gulf War in the name of the New World Order. My wife, Lady Antonia, has ordered a salmon mousse to start with, shaped like a Scud Missile. We are then having the traditional Christmas Turkey but I have made it perfectly clear that we will none of us eat a mouthful for as long as there are still political prisoners being tortured in the prisons of Turkey. We will have traditional Christmas crackers with the mince pies containing paper armbands and seasonal riddles such as:

Q: Why is the USA an imperialist warmonger intent on subjugating all Third World nations by removing all their powers of self-determination?

A: Because it bloody is. It's so bloody obvious I'm not prepared to bloody discuss it further.

Incidentally, as a gesture of support

for the Birmingham 6, plus the Guildford 4, plus the Tottenham 3, plus the Liverpool 8, we will be serving a '21 Port with the cigars.

For the past six months I have been working on a new thirty-second play about torture in Holland Park. Okay, okay, these days there isn't a lot of torture in Holland Park. So let no one try and tell you my plays don't get things changed.

Contrary to the malignant disinformation spread by the propagandist forces of the present administration, the June 20th Group is still going strong. Its meetings, I must tell you, have never been more constructive, never more single-minded in their determination to bring down the cold-blooded torturers and mass-murderers who at present speak in our names.

Inevitably there have been one or two changes to the personnel structure of the group. I suspected a leak to the fascist press from the Bragg enclave, so I was forced to sever all relations with them. Through a close reading of the newspapers, I discovered that the Holroyd/Drabble/Greer/Weldon pressure-group had perpetrated a hypocritical deceit on the rest of us, two of them — Holroyd and Drabble — having been married five years before. So I washed my hands of them. At an early meeting at the River Café, John Mortimer wished to veto my resolution condemning the junta in Nicaragua in order to push through a motion urging second helpings of puds all round. This was the last straw. "Get your coat, Lady Antonia. I'm not taking any more of this crap. We're leaving," I said. And so we split with Mortimer too. Finally, Hare and McEwan disagreed with me over my support for an out-and-out condemnation of Vaclav Havel for sending good

wishes to Mrs Bloody Thatcher on her retirement, and Rushdie can never be bothered to turn up, so we're not seeing them any more. So the June 20th Group is left with a strong kernel of supporters — never stronger in my opinion — formed of:

1) **Harold Pinter**
2) **Lady Antonia Fraser**
with:
3) **Lady Elizabeth Anson**

(the latter being employed as the Official Outsider Caterer to the June 20th Group, specifically to handle food and seating arrangements). These days, Antonia is finding she has to spend more and more time researching her new Jemima Shore series, so the group discussions are generally attended by myself alone. And let me tell you this: we are *angry*.

Ordinary life is filled with the threat of a lurking menace. Everywhere, the nuances of everyday conversation contain gaps behind which the unknowable prowls, unseen and unheard, ready to spring out. Yesterday, I was sitting at my desk, a man of sixty. A sudden howl filled the air. Relentless, interminable. Then — bang, bang, bang — a machine was knocking, again and again, against the door. Whooooooo! BANG! BANG! BANG! Whoooooo! The howl. The knocking. Was it Them? What did They want? What would They do to me?

I moved to the door.

I opened it.

"Ah, Fatima." It was our Filipina doing a spot of hoovering. "You're a lurking menace!" I thundered. "C'mon, Antonia, we're not staying here, we're bloody going, get your coat!"

NED SHERRIN

This was the week in which it was announced that Prince Charles had given up polo for golf — a case of going for a Hole In One, perhaps, or not as the case may be, so let's swiftly recall that this was the week in which Mr Robert Maxwell's raincoat was returned from the cleaners: a sure sign, one might think, that Robert's Mac's Well! and so let's pass rapidly on to a new book about Adolf Hitler in which the author claims that the Führer was something of a perfectionist: one might almost say that he wanted to get it Reich First Time, but now let us turn without due let or hindrance to the Diary Proper, and one must hope that one is not also a "Diary Pooper", not to be mistaken, of course, for "Diana Cooper", the legendary beauty who is sadly no longer with us, unlike my five studio guests this week!

I am, I fancy, known as something of the *enfant terrible* of the theatre, and to this end I have compiled a wicked volume of theatrical anecdotes (available at all good bookshops now — hurry, hurry! — and excuse my plug, as Robert Mitchum was once heard to say come bathtime!). My own favourites? Tricky quessie, as the late Hermione Gingold might have said, but I would finally have to pick a gem from the legends surrounding the great Sir John Gielgud. These I call my "Gielgoodies", and most of them tell one something of that fine actor's propensity for the Dropped Brick. If your appetite needs whetting, take a nibble, if you will, at this:

Upon hearing that the then Sir Laurence Olivier was to star as Hamlet opposite the great Vivien Leigh, Sir John, somewhat hard-of-hearing, was heard to exclaim, "I'm sorry — I didn't catch what you said"!! The information having been diligently repeated, Sir John, famously forgetful, said, "I forgot — have they performed together before?" In fact, the glamorous couple had been married a full six months at the time of this inapposite remark!!

Following a disastrous first night in *The Tempest*, Sir John, as forgetful as ever, was heard to say, "Let's hope the third night goes better!" On being told that there was still the *second* night to go, he issued the following gem: "*Good Lord — so there is!*"

I have come — for my sins — to be known as the Godfather of the great Sixties Satire boom. Heady days, indeed. I was then producing the legendary *That Was The Week That Was*, better known to one and all as *TW3*. Week after week, we took razor-sharp lunges at some of the most esteemed Sacred Cows of the day — and somehow lived to tell the tale! I remember well a sketch involving dear Milly Martin and my old friend David Frost (whatever happened to David, I wonder?!! — only kidding, David!) in which Harold Macmillan was bitterly attacked in the following sparklingly savage repartee:

David: The Prime Minister, Mr Harold Macmillan, announced today that Britain was in the *red*.

Milly: And that, David, must be why he feels *blue!* (LAUGHTER)

David: Yes, but let's not criticise him for being *yellow!* (LAUGHTER)

Milly: After all, he's making his rivals quite *green* (with envy)!!! (LAUGHTER and fade to blackout).

Lance Percival *(singing to calypso rhythm)*:

Oh, The PM says he's oh-so-blue
He's a funny fella — it's true
Doo-bee-doo-bee-doo-bee-doooo!
Oh, yes, The PM says he's... blue!!

Sketches such as this shook the establishment to its very core, and ushered in the social revolution of the 1960s. I suppose if one wanted to be pompous one would say that one changed British society forever with one's wit and irreverence, but one had no idea at the time that what one was doing was so historic. There were complaints, of course — particularly when David Frost described the then Home Secretary, Henry Brooke, in a satirical aside, as "Brooke-ing no opposition" — but we fought the good fight. These days, the same rich anti-establishment satirical spirit survives, for my money, in the persons of Robert Elms and Carol Thatcher on Radio 4's *Ned Sherrin's Loose Ends*.

The late Coral Browne did much to conceal her extraordinary kindness and generosity of spirit. Upon seeing the delicious Diana Rigg making her first entrance as Hedda Gabler in Strindberg's great play *The Doll's House*, she could not "button her lip", as young Robert Elms might have put it. "My God!" she turned to me and bellowed. "Diana always did have fat legs, darling!"

To dinner at the Caprice with Gore Vidal and a couple of young friends. As usual, Gore is in excellent form and needs little prompting to display the full range of his exquisitely caustic tongue. On Nancy Reagan: "I believe she was once married to an actor." On Margaret Thatcher: "Poor old Margaret." On Great Britain: "A forgotten little country situated somewhere off the coast of Normandy." On Martin Amis: "Poor little Martin." On European Monetary Union: "Frankly, it doesn't keep me awake at night." On President Bush: "Poor old George." On Norman Mailer: "Poor old Norman." On Jesus Christ: "Poor old Jesus."

Needless to say, we are all in *fits* at these witty and waspish *bon mots*. "I will always remember," I chip in, as the laughter subsides, "having cocktails with the late Gertrude Lawrence and the legendary Alan Jay Lerner, composer of *Dotty About Dishes*, *Make Mine Sixpence*, and *Dreaming of Dahlias*, before a party thrown by that admirable all-round thespian Nyree Dawn Porter for the magical Evelyn Laye at which, as I remember, the lovely Maggie Smith and the much under-rated Pet Clark were to be seen talking to the splendid Shelley Winters, then starring with dear Glynis Johns in *Whistling Wildly Through the Wisteria* at the Aldwych, when who should walk in but the unstoppable Tyrone Guthrie accompanied by the sharp-tongued but resourceful Dame Alicia Markova, who was about to regale us all with an anecdote concerning unmentionable goings-on between my favourite old trouper Fenella Fielding and —"

At this moment, I look mischievously around at my audience in order to heighten the comic effect. They are nowhere to be seen. The maître d' bustles over. "They left for a club 'alf an 'our ago, m'sieur," he tells me. "But they told me to tell you they will be back before the punchline." Sure enough, they reappear twenty minutes later, right on time for the end: "And Coral turned to me and bellowed, 'My God, Diana always did have fat legs, darling!' " I open the laughter, and in less than thirty seconds, they have all joined in, proving once again that the Satire Boom is far from over.

HRH QUEEN ELIZABETH THE QUEEN MOTHER

My favourite chocolates are Orange Creme, Strawberry Creme, Nougat and — you must think me *awfully* wicked — a Brandy Truffle. In bed, I stick with Maltesers, in the bathroom it's always a Marathon bar, but never more than three. I find Sherbet Fountains go deliciously well with my 5.30 Whisky(s!) and Soda with *Neighbours*.

Have you watched *Neighbours*? You *must*. I've always had a special place in my heart for the poor people in the East End of London and that's where it's set. They all have the most delicious Cockney accents, reminding me of the time I visited the brave little East End during the war. It seems much sunnier now, I must say, so perhaps I will visit it again soon. They absolutely adore the Royal Family there, you know, bless them, because we lend colour to their lives.

What an awful brouhaha there has been in my *Daily Express* about the way an odd little man called Woodrow Wyatt has published snippets of a conversation with me. Alas, I remember so little about him, though I remember thinking he was rather small and rather fat, very, very pompous and — forgive me — a little nondescript. And he would *insist* upon puffing his cigar into my face as he held forth about this and that. If he is going to tell tales, then I'm afraid I've instructed my people to strike him off my list of possibles.

At the same dinner, I met another writer — A.N. Something-or-other, who seemed much more the ticket, certainly not the "blabbing" sort, but discreet and respectful. I wonder if he'd care to write my biography?

I have always loved writers. And waiters. Writers and waiters, waiters and writers. Too adorable. Of the two, I think I prefer waiters, because at least they bring one things. We occasionally hire a waiter called Worsthorne who manages to write in his spare time and will *insist* on regaling us all with what he has written that week when he should be clearing away, the poor thing. Once, he even sat down to table with us!! Marvellous old character, though. I rather think he comes from the East End. It's full of them, you know. He may well be a "Pearly King". So exciting.

In my time, I've had the very great pleasure of entertaining some of the most superbly brilliant men and ladies this nation has ever produced. Sir Noel Coward, Sir Cecil Beaton, Sir Hardy Amies, the lot. I recall one dinner party with particular pleasure. Sir Roy Strong, the gifted painter, sat to my left, with Lord St John of Fawnsley, the impersonator, to my right. For some reason, artists have always been so very fond of one, and others present had been hand-picked from the cream of the arts, including Mr Eric Sykes, the comedian, my granddaughter, lovely Sarah York, who has written children's books, poor girl, and Sir Kingsley Amis, the actor. They simply couldn't stop singing my praises, perfectly sweet of them, and as Worsthorne brought around the Toffee Crisps and the top-ups I decided to award a dear little prize to whoever could praise me most beautifully in a maximum of time of sixty seconds.

Oh, the fun we had! I kept time and scored whilst my dear guests "pitted their wits" against one another to come up with the most adorable compliments. The winner? Lord St John of Fawnsley, who called me many charming things, comparing me to a jewel, a flower, a perfectly formed young tennis champion, a rhododendron in full bloom, a mint edition *Almanac de Gotha* and a *crème caramel*, all in one breath, bless him. Amis, poor little man, could think of nothing better than to say I wasn't half as bad as Major Ferguson. I'm awfully sorry, I don't think we'll be inviting him again, not if he doesn't know how to behave, such a shame.

Items in my handbag: tissues; chocolates (Rollos, Wrigley's Spearmint "Gum"); one miniature Gordon's (for emergencies!); one spare string of pearls; one copy the *Sporting Life*; a toothbrush; spare pair jeans for leisurewear; the day's "horoscope" from the *Daily Express*; one tin, Heinz "Alphabetti Spaghetti"; one "good luck charm" (darling dolly of dear Mrs Simpson, plus the sweetest little pins!); yesterday's slips from my bookmaker; two packets chocolate eclairs; twelve thousand five hundred in cash (just in case).

I'm a great collector of words. It's one of my interests. One is so often so lucky to be in the company of very, very brainy people (Nicholas Soames, my grandson Edward, and many more) and they are teaching one new words all the time. "Kew" for instance. Did you know that there are some parts of the world where if everyone wants something at the same time — a Bittermint, say — they have to "form a Kew", which means standing in a line for a little while. Such fun. And "Soupymarket", that's another, based on *the* most extraordinary idea. Obviously one knows about "shops", where ordinary people — largely from our dear East End, I would imagine — offer coins in exchange for a Milky Bar — but a "Soupymarket" is much, much bigger than a "shop", with tins piled high, mainly of broth, hence the name. People — how I wish they wouldn't mutter about one so — sometimes criticise our wonderful Royal Family for living a "sheltered life", but this is most unhelpful and quite untrue. I opened a "Soupymarket" and walked around it six years ago, somewhere in the East End, I would imagine, my driver doesn't tell me these things! Their most charming aspect, I learnt from my experience, is that they let each individual "shopper" walk along the aisles in the company of a manager with no one else allowed in until they have finished. *Such* a civilised idea.

One more very clever new word, if you'll forgive me, so kind. "Dear Swosher". I feel quite sure you haven't heard of that one! It seems that if the kind women who clean your dinner plates for you are on holiday or feeling a little poorly — you know what they are! — then it is possible to employ a "Dear Swosher", which is a sort of mechanical appliance for cleaning dirty dinner plates. The modern world! Such fun, don't you think?

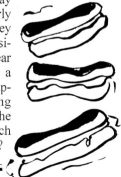

MADONNA

Okay, so my life's a very private thing, like I'm coming to terms with religion in a big way just now and that's a very private thing and I want to make it as public as I can so as to help others in my situation, right?

I'm an artist, I'm obsessed, I put all of myself into my work. Like, my new song, *Whoo! Touch My Sex!* is basically about my struggle to come to terms with my childhood, and the Roman Catholic church and my obsessions with guilt and with insecurity, and it represents one of my most complex statements of self-revelation so far. So the lyric goes:

I wanna screw you, screw you
All thru the nite, nite
Wanna get thru to you
Let's do it right, right
(Chorus) Whoo! Touch my sex!
Thats outasight
Whoo! Touch my sex! Touch my sex!
Turn on my life!

Well, I'm delving very deep into myself there, I'm exploring my unconscious paranoias in a way I've never allowed myself before, and I think it represents like a very clear and positive statement about the way I am now, you know, and I think that should help a lot of people who are still searching, I guess we're all searching for something.

I'm at present devoting my emotional and artistic resources towards creating an ambient stage environment for my next World Tour. Like, I'm obsessed with black at the moment, like it means night and death and mystery and pepsi, right? So we're gonna start off with just this black curtain, and the black curtain will rise to reveal a stage totally black, okay? And then I'll be carried on by these six black guys, right? And I'll be dressed all in black with black hair and a black mask, and the thing is no one in the audience will know I'm even on stage for over forty minutes so it'll be like church or something and then I'll sing my new number, *Spank My Butt (All Day Long)* and it'll be like Picasso and Dali and Bosch and the Pope and Sigmund Freud all rolled into one, just incredibly powerful and traumatic.

People are always wanting to know about my art collection. It's a very private collection, very personal. I mean it means a lot to me so I don't want to open it up to the world, know what I mean?, but I have a Dali, and I have a Daily too, she helps me clean up, and I have a Picasso of a cup of tea, from his Brew Period I suppose, and I have a really beautiful Frida Kahlo of a nostril with a spider in it and another outasight one by Frida Kahlo of a woman's hand with its fingers chopped off and ants all over it which is like a really positive image for all women and gays. I guess Frida was just too beautiful for this world.

My real favourite artist at the moment is a guy from years back, Italian like me, called René Sonce, like he painted lots of Jesuses on the Cross and Jesuses as a baby and angels and blah blah and he painted literally hundreds of the other Madonna, the one before me, in fact it was he who made the other Madonna into a big deal, like before he discovered her she couldn't sing and you never see pictures of her even dancing, like I guess her career had a setback what with that baby, but René saw through all that bullshit and he made her into a really big star, like you see his pictures of her in every gallery in the world and she's not even dressed that great, like maybe she had a weight problem. The pressures on her from fans must have been amazing, and she most likely had to learn to come to terms with herself, so I identify with her one helluva lot, though as far as I know she never produced a video, lousy marketing department I guess.

I was giving a rare interview the other day and I said to the interviewer, I can only spare another ten minutes, you know, I've got three more rare interviews to give before I have my shredded carrot for lunch, then I got my two-hour workout, then there's another four rare interviews before I become an essentially very private person all over again for a photographer from *People* magazine. So he says, "Tell me about the hidden Madonna, the Madonna nobody knows, the very private and reclusive Madonna, the Madonna who's alone in her apartment with her fears and obsessions," and I say, "Jeez, that's the side of Madonna I keep from the world, the side that was totally wrecked by my marriage to Sean Penn, the side that is coming to terms with Catholic guilt, the side that can't seem to hold down a conventional relationship because she feels so open to misunderstanding, the side whose whole private life is in a constant state of disarray, the side that couldn't handle Warren Beatty looking at other women, the side that feels the need for reassurance from the public yet is always at the same time in retreat, you wanna know about that side?" And the interviewer, he says, yeah, tell us about that side of Madonna, and I say, "Sorry, I never talk to anyone about that side, it's totally, totally, *totally* private." Like, otherwise, your whole life becomes public property, you know?

I've been designing my own costume for my next video to accompany my new single, *Pump Your Stuff, Big Boy*. I've gone for a complete change of image to reflect a whole new outlook in my emotional and spiritual development.

When I recorded my massive worldwide hit, *Let My Fingers Feel Your Body (Krishna Krishna)*, I was really into Zen Buddhism, and my stage costume — a leather G-string with spiked brassiere and fishnet tights — seemed to draw on this very Eastern approach to my religious fears and obsessions.

Then I was seriously into feminist studies and the role of oppressed woman in the 20th century when my next big hit, *Find Me a Guy (Who Wants Me Bad)*, came out, so I changed my costume to present a positive image for women everywhere — a rubber bondage-style body-stocking with high heels.

Finally, I was reading up a helluva lot on vegetarianism in the 1990s, and I wanted to make a strong pro-vegetarian statement, so I recorded my biggest hit yet, *Suck! Suck! Suck! (You're Mine Tonite)*, wearing a specially designed costume of lurex brassiere and suede thong.

Pump Your Stuff, Big Boy is basically about the insanity of celebrity and the urban nightmare of 21st century society, and to express this in costume I have had Gaultier make me something totally different, like a real break with the past. It's an all-black PVC clingshirt with leather straps, and it exposes a sexual side of my art and my personality which I have previously been too insecure to portray before. It's an entirely new me — obsessive, reclusive, concerned and very, very private.

TERRY WOGAN

'Tis an ill wind, as me old mammy used to say. Come a month or two, and old Tel here will be presenting most pulchritudinously his very last show of that fully phantasmagorical — now there's a word for the old knapsack — thrice-weekly show called simply *Wogan*, yes, 'tis indeed.

Seven years. Ho hum. Can it really be seven years? It can indeed, indeed it can. Seven years. Well, fancy that. Seven years at the cutting edge. Well bless me cotton socks. To be a little bit serious just for one moment, I suspect that dear old Auntie Beeb might have more trouble than she'd have us believe at finding a replacement quite as on-the-ball as yours truly, but that's another matter entirely. Too many hosts these days are, in my own humble opinion, rather too content to waffle on. But then that's the way the wind blows across the strawberry patch, as me old Irish granny used to tell us.

I was always more of a writer, more of a scintillating scrivener or weary-eyed wordsmith, than a star of the old magic lantern, so I'm delighted to seize this opportunity to remind myself and my readers, in Shakespeare's own dear language, of some of the highlights of my career in your sitting-room and on your hearth-rug. Let me unbutton the old jacket — ah, that's better — slump into the old easy-chair, take up the wondrous old Wogan quill, and begin:

I've long held a soft spot in the old ticker for actors and actresses, thespians all, and it's been my privilege o'er the past seven years to get to know some of these thrillin' theatricals on the old prog.

Ah, memories, memories. I remember asking dear old Jimmy Stewart — the late, great James Stewart — whether he was often recognised in public, and whether he had any thoughts on the matter.

Then I asked that easy-on-the-eye actress and singer-songwriter Cher how she first started off in the business.

And when the great Bob Hope came onto the show, I couldn't let him go without asking him whether "Bob Hope" was indeed his real name.

Dean Martin? Yes, I met him too, and my first question to him was whether he had always wanted to be a singer.

And I asked his old pal the great Sammy Davis Jr to explain just how he'd managed to stay at the top for so long. Good questions all, and everyone of 'em came back with a surprising revelation or amusing anecdote, as befits their superstar status.

What was it they said, I hear you ask! To be honest, at this distance in time, I forget their actual replies, but they were all thorough professionals, and our conversations — a bit of the old "verbal parrying", you might say — made for some of the most memorable shows in the series. Ho hum.

I like to think, in my own humble wee way, as my Scots grandpappy might put it, that I played an equally deft hand when it came to setting some of our top politicos at their ease. Often it's what I call the sideways question — the question they might not have been asked before, and they may well not be expecting — that is most revealing. Get 'em off their guard, and you can unearth some pretty telling revelations: that's old Tel's merry motto.

Let me give you a f 'rinstance: when ex-Premier Edward Heath came on the old prog, I wanted to ask him what he really thought of his old rival Mrs T. As he sat down, I judged the time was right and I asked him, bold as the proverbial brass, if he had always favoured the lightweight, single-breasted suit. "Yes," he replied. "I find them easier for travelling, and they don't get too hot." We then spent the next four-and-a-half minutes chatting about clothes — socks, shirts, ties, we covered the lot.

To many viewers, it was a revelation, showing Heath in a lovely new light as a man who knew a bit or two about clothes. Of course, it left no time to ask him about his old rival Mrs T because petite Sheena Easton was scheduled to come on to give her latest number the old one-two, but Ted Heath's feelings towards that much-maligned lady are his own affair, and he told me privately afterwards that he's sick to death with press intrusion on the matter. Hear, hear, quoth I — let's not take curiosity too far, fellas.

A̲t heart, I remain the cheery chap from the fine old City of Limerick in the Emerald Isle, a fellow who likes to earn an honest penny, so I'm always interested to meet chaps who have a brass farthing or three to rub together, to coin a proverbial phrase.

"I don't mean to pry, Robert," I said to roly-poly publisher Robert Maxwell when he was a guest on the show a couple o' years back, "but you must be worth a bob or two. And yet at heart you remain a family man with simple tastes, am I right?" I remember he gave me a

lovely warm smile and said that I had hit the nail on the head.

I was always fascinated to meet millionaires with their own companies and houses on the River, so different from the rest of us bare-footed paupers. "I suppose you can eat in all the best restaurants and buy quality bottles of the old vino," I said to the Duke of Westminster in 1987. Ivana Trump, sometime better half of Donald Trump, agreed with me when I said that it must be lovely having all that extra dough so as to give some to your favourite charity. Ah, well — we can't all be as rich as Croesus, that marvellously mythical fellow — but it's fun to find out about those who are!

T̲o be perfectly frank — and why not, I ask myself?! — it's been many moons since I've troubled these dear little legs o' mine to take me into the *Wogan* theatre. Save yourself the shoe-leather, Terence, old chap, I told myself three years ago, and I haven't set foot in the theatre since, preferring to relax 'midst family and furry friends, basking in the dappled glades of Taplow, Bucks.

Bend back your lugholes, and I'll explain. Ever wondered why the Tel you see on the gogglebox has more of the old hair than he did three years back? Y'see, long ago, it dawned on me that I only ever asked the same six questions, whoever I was interviewing. If it were a politician, I asked him how he liked to relax, if it were a soap star I asked her whether she'd ever been mistaken for her character in real life, and so on. Hey presto, Bob's your uncle and toodle-oo, I arranged for old film of yours truly, asking these very same questions, to be played to all my new guests, thus preventing any need for old Tel himself to turn up! Result? A carefree show, as lively as a tender young lamb in spring. Whoops! My time's run out. Cheerio!

GORE VIDAL

How very pleasant, as Henry James would doubtless have said, to be writing for one of gorgeously insignificant little England's still less significant publications. England is — how shall I put it? — a nation akin to Guatemala in importance, though with rather less sun to give one's unblemished skin that necessary bronze. Nevertheless, as Huxley might have said, nevertheless she is worth a pardonable glimpse from time to time, if only to establish that she is still there, her grotesque visage still poking gamely through the waves, before going under for ever.

Fitzgerald, poor Fitzgerald; the paltry beefcake Hemingway; demented little Faulkner; Melville, dreary, dogged, archbore Melville; I daresay there has been a greater American writer than Vidal, but if there is I have yet to wade through his work. But I not only write Vidal; unlike so many others, I read him too. I am the historian, and, even my sternest critics would argue, the inventor, of the United States of America, the chronicler of its architects, the greatest among them myself. I create vast masterpieces like *Burr*, my remarkable 800-page history of the American Telephone System, I have used my — how shall I put it? — genius to transform that sprawling, divinely crumbling empire into an exquisite work of art.

Interviewers and telepersonages daily make the pilgrimage to my villa in Sancho Panza's Italy. They like to ask me, in their bewilderingly monosyllabic fashion, how I can be so sure that the United States of Oblivion, as I have with no little wit termed it (!), is fast becoming a sub-literate continent. "Tell me, my dear," I reply, if the interviewer is a man, "do you know how many copies my last novel sold in the entire USA?" I show him the sales figures, just over seventeen in hardback. "And you are claiming, I believe, madam, that this is a civilised — that is, functionally literate — nation?" Silence ensues. A nation that prefers Erich Segal to Gore Vidal will soon flutter away into nothingness, like a false eyelash placed by an indifferent hand upon the face of a sweating gentleman.

I note with interest that your dear darling Queen Mother is soon to be ninety. Truman Capote, it will be remembered, claimed to have conducted a turbulent affair with the sweet thing whilst staying with Noel Coward at Portofino in '51. It was dark, and he was under the impression she was Prince Philip, or so he claimed. But Capote was not, as Forster might have said, to be trusted. Capote claimed to have enjoyed sexual gymnastics, as one might say, with, among others, W. Somerset Maugham, J.B. Priestley, Major Ronald Ferguson, Lord Hailsham, Ray Allan and Lord Charles, William Golding, William Rees-Mogg, Nana Mouskouri, Mr Mooney from *The Lucy Show*, Leonard Nimoy, Harold Pinter, Reginald Varney and Burl Ives, but I rather wonder. If he had spent less time inventing affairs and more time moving his pen in its ineffably tiresome way across paper he might have rivalled Henry James and myself. As it is, he is dead, and can invent no more; a mercy to his readers, and a great boon to his punctuation. Truman never could master that full stop.

My wit is, as Harriet Beecher Stowe might put it, legendary. At a discreet dinner party last October, I greatly amused the assembled company of the very rich and powerful people whom I number among my acquaintances by saying, when the fruit salad was passed, "So many pineapples, my dear!" This has since entered the anthologies. Again, at a garden party thrown by senior Italian royalty last month, I caused humorous uproar by pointing to the beautifully mown lawn and saying: "A beautifully mown lawn; why, that reminds me of my old friend Nancy Reagan!" Consequently, I am often in demand on television chat shows as one of the very few American minds still ticking. I recently described President Bush as "that curious little man", your own dear Mrs Thatcher as "a woman, oh, yes, very much a woman, I'm afraid", Deng Xiao Ping as "that by no means unwizened little Chinaman", William Shakespeare as "that over-reaching punster", and Jesus Christ as "the hirsute Jewish woodworker so given to the futile gesture". It is in the spirit of the age to ignore such brilliantly pointed criticism of what those eager little sociologists call Society. This is why I remain in exile from my own land, my own people having refused me the office of Presidency on account of my cleverness.

I daresay subscribers to this naughty, smackworthy magazine will be looking forward to reading my current diagnosis of what ails your charmingly backward little third world island. I understand the powerful, and I possess a thorough understanding of current English political life, so I imagine there might be people — just one or two, forgive my irony — less qualified to prognosticate. The owners of the Disunited Kingdom, as I once waspishly

termed it, will soon tire of the Woman Thatcher with her intolerable femininity. So as to promote the illusion of democracy, they will hold a General Election, and then they will install the Leader of the Labour Party, Harold Wilson, in office, with George Brown as their compliant Foreign Secretary, who will do his darnedest to push the country into the European Economic Community. This is, as Edith Wharton might have put it, only a prediction, but I am widely credited, even by my sworn enemies, for having my finger caressingly but firmly on the pulse of World Events.

Of course, my honesty does me no good with the English, who have rarely shown an inclination for the truth. England shies away from men of influence like a scullery boy from an errant hand. President Kennedy, on the other hand, knew well to listen to the great American author. "John, my dear," I whispered into his almost perfect ear on the White House balcony one sultry afternoon. "A few words of advice on how best to run the country... "

"Who let this poisonous mincing faggot in?" he replied, but he still listened with keen interest to my at times scathing diagnosis as the door slammed firmly behind me, and my influence lingers still.

GERMAINE GREER

My God, I despair of women sometimes. My whole life and my every breath has been informed with the imprint of my love and respect, admiration indeed, of women. But for Christ's sake, they sometimes let me down. If there is one type of woman I hate it is the very thin type of woman. And if there is another type of woman who gets up my nose it's the fatty. And what about those detestable in-betweenies, those spineless wretches who don't have the guts to be one thing or the other? They frankly get on my wick. Not until woman can truly be herself — neither fat nor thin nor in-between — can our sisterhood hope to save this doomed planet.

Sometimes I think I care too much. I can't help feeling passionately about the future of this planet and all the heads on it, and I constantly strive to take a forward-thinking and progressive view — okay, revolutionary — to the fuzz and the establishment and how they get their rocks off.

Over the years, my radical intellectual approach to the issues of the day has done as much as anyone to make this world a better place. Witness my articles "There's a Dick in my Toaster and The Pigs Don't give a Fuck" (*Oz*, Sept '69). "Vaginal Deodorants Are Murdering the Ozone Layer" (*Independent* Magazine, July '89) and "Hands Off My Arse, Fat Boy (A Prayer for Bangladesh)" (*Screw* Magazine, June '73). The pieces I wrote at that time still make great reading because unlike some others I can think of I can write much better than them punchy sentences that get my point over without using too much of sensation-seeking words like fuck or cock, for God's sake.

Let's address ourselves to some real live issues, just this once, for God's sake. Jimi Hendrix may not have wanted us to grieve for him but we had better grieve for ourselves. We have lost the best rock guitarist we ever had because we did not know how to keep him. If Jimi is going to live tomorrow we have to make up our minds to live today. He was playing real good for free and he was happy but we let him slip down the energy drain. Can we build fast enough to close it before we disappear ourselves? Can we sweep up the pieces of yesterday's life?

I live from the earth, and with my spade I give back to the earth that which is rightfully the earth's: earth for instance.

I love chickens, and I keep chickens not just to strangle them but to provide food and to EDUCATE, for God's sake. I find it shameful that so few chickens know the first thing about what they're doing on this planet so at 9.30 every morning I assemble them in a classroom and sweat my guts out trying to stamp out their ignorance. You know, half of them couldn't even tell you the name of the Almighty, and the other half would fuck up on the spelling, making it "Germane" without the "i".

Forthcoming opinions: "Stinging Nettles Make Perfect Table-Settings", "Charity Sucks", "Let's Get Outta Vietnam Now", "MacGovern's The Man".

There's not much on earth that I hate more than I hate what I hate about chickens which is why I hate chickens more than I hate what I hate about the rest of the earth. By shameless use of contacts and endless plugging of their ridiculous clucking, by their ostentatious eggs (haven't they even heard of the word ABORTION for God's sake?) and their feathers and their look-at-me-I'm-so-fucking-humble expressions, they have managed to convince normally sane people that they are not the unabashed imperialist poultry-supremacists who would happily kill us if they had the Bomb which thank God they don't.

When you are the centre of attention, it is easy to act humble. The stereotype chicken imposed by poultry society — not much up top, good to eat with gravy, etcetera — is far removed from the squalid reality of sharp beaks, sweat-sodden bodies and vicious, blood-stained claws. All this must change. Now. So this term I've given each of them a copy of my last book, *Sex and Destiny*, to inwardly digest before returning it to the earth. Only when we have a 100% literate chicken population can we really feel free as humans.

In my house we operate a strict Green policy. We recycle everything we can. I recycle books, opinions, articles and even diary items, some of which I originally employed as far back as the mid-Sixties. Of course, natural resources are growing less as each day passes, and there is now a very real possibility that by, say, the year 2000, all my views, pseudo-historical surveys and dogmas will have run dry. To avoid this possibility, I have taken to using marvellous thought-substitutes. I find, for instance, that self-righteous scorn is a perfectly acceptable alternative to serious criticism, and that a barked insult can easily be passed off as wit. Another method is to turn over all the thoughts you had ten years ago and to use them again the other way up. No one will notice, for

---

★ STAR THOUGHTS ★

PADDY ASHDOWN MP

Let us as Liberal Democrats say this loudly and clearly. Let us take this message of ours to the heart of the country. Let us turn around and say that we are no more a party of looking backwards than we are a party of standing still. We want to engage in the battle of ideas. We want to stand up and be counted. We want to say to our children's children, we are your grandparents. We are the party of optimism, of realism, of dynamism, of freedom. We have a very real determination to combine the old with the new, the future with the past. Our message is that our message is a message which deserves to be taken to the very heart of this nation. Let us have the courage to pick up our roots, to hold them up high in the air and to say to the British people with one voice — this tree will never die!

God's sake. But if, like me, you are growing a crop of lovely fresh banalities, do be sure to keep them well-fed with good fresh dollops of manure and household gubbins. I have a gorgeous crop of opinion-pieces sprouting shortly — among them "Fellatio Causes Cancer", "Let's Stop This 'Being Nice' Bullshit" and "The Only Answer: A Condom for the Ozone Layer" — and I am delighted to say that they will be grown entirely from regurgitated waste.

JENNIFER'S RETIREMENT DIARY

After a night in bed, I entered the kitchen of the flat to pour myself some quite excellent All Bran from one of Mr Kellogg's very sensible packets, beautifully designed, and then poured Mr Unigate's delicious milk on top of it, making a thoroughly pleasant breakfast, perhaps one of the most enjoyable I have ever attended.

I then began to plot my day. Looking up at my mantelpiece, I noticed that my invitations to parties thrown by my delightful and excellently-bred friends all stopped by coincidence on the very day of my retirement from the splendid *Harpers and Queen* magazine. Nevertheless, I knew that my presence would be required at five or six major society events, so, after a delicious cup of coffee courtesy of Mr G. Blend, I ventured onto the streets of our very own dear city of London.

My first call of the day was on a beautifully organised and most impressive Employment Exchange where glorious postcards let one know exactly the employment that is on offer in the Mayfair locality. Joining an impressive queue, I discovered that there were one or two fellow guests I failed to recognise, so I got out my notebook and inquired as to their names. These most helpful people included Quit Shuvvin and his son Piss Awf, Ooyoo Starin-Att, looking resplendent in a brown and dark brown "boiler suit" with exotic phlegm inlay, Upyors Mite accompanied by his attractive wife Gorblimey Mite, the Fuck-

this-Foralark family, looking better than ever, and the Hon. and Mrs Buggerov, who graciously offered me an antique "coca-cola" can to nibble while we waited. I was also delighted to make the acquaintance of O. God Almighty, sporting an attractive string vest and a pair of casual trousers just beneath the buttocks.

I then set off to a luncheon party thrown by some very dear friends at the Connaught Hotel. Oddly enough, Her Majesty's Postal Service had failed to deliver my invitation but I knew that if I put my head around the door I would be welcomed with open arms as I have been these past forty years. I was greeted, as always, by the head doorman, Charles, who most considerately placed himself in front of me and asked if he could possibly help. I informed him that I was expected at a party thrown by some very dear friends, and he checked a list he held on a most useful clipboard. He then called a larger doorman and most kindly asked him to escort me out of the door. Within a matter of seconds, I had been whisked with utmost efficiency back out through the revolving doors, accompanied by charming wishes for my good riddance. I remained on the street outside the hotel — a most original idea for a party location, I must say, and very greatly appreciated — for the duration of the party, which, it emerged, was in Fancy Dress, such an amusing idea, with many people coming as road-sweepers, dustbin-men and the like. From my grandstand position just near the gutter, I spotted The Duke and Duchess of Abercrombie, The Hon. Miss Lucinda Northampton, and The Countess Ruislip, resplendent in a very pretty dress of azalea silk georgette, but they seemed to be going into another party indoors, so they obviously failed to notice me waving and shouting "coo-eee". All in all a delightful evening, and so clever to "do away with" drinks and cocktail-eats, which so often lead to unnecessary expense for the host and hostess.

I then went to see my old friends the Sainsburys, picking up a most attractive metal "basket" as I entered. I saw a lot of very old and dear friends in this charming building — so cleverly designed! — among them The Prince and Princess of Wales, Miss Anouska Hempel, The Earl and Countess Spencer, Lady Tryon looking radiant in pink, Sir Hugh Casson, Lord Hailsham, Lord and Lady Whitelaw, Mr Roger Moore and The Duke and Duchess of Westminster, looking younger than ever. A kindly assistant then asked whether I was planning to buy the copy of *Hello!* magazine I had been observing all my very old and dear friends in, but I decided against, and moved on towards the delightful "Household Products" counter, with its excellent range of quality goods: such a clever idea of the delightful Sainsburys and so handy for all their many devoted friends.

Returning to change at my flat, I found that my old friends the Bailiffs, Ron, Don, Len and also Ben had called in my absence, such a shame, but they had kindly left a small memento of their visit on the outer door, a padlock crafted in silver metal, with an enchanting chain. I then walked to the arches at Charing Cross, where I had watched our own dear Prince and Princess of Wales parade to St Paul's for their triumphant marriage in 1981 on the most memorable day in our nation's history. At seven o'clock promptly, the caterers generously served piping hot soup and a bread roll to all guests, who then returned to the relaxing and historic surrounds of the arches, where they each found a most welcoming cardboard box to keep out the slight chill of the evening. On the side of my own most effective box was printed "HEINZ", a memory of very dear friends of that name who have entertained me so lavishly in Washington on each of my visits there.

The next morning, I was offered a delicious breakfast of Cider and Methylated Spirits mixed with one of Mr Carlsberg's most invigorating Special Brews by an old and very rank friend, but I regretfully declined. I went behind my cardboard box to change, and from there walked to Clarence House, London home of my very dear old friend, the tremendously youthful and much-loved by all the nations of the world possibly the most gracious woman who has ever lived the ever-radiant Queen Elizabeth the Queen Mother, and rang the front doorbell of this most delightful mansion. As a most original welcoming treat, I was then surrounded by four policemen in very smart uniforms, all pointing beautifully polished pistols in my direction. When I pointed out that Queen Elizabeth the Queen Mother was one of my very oldest and dearest friends, they told me that I was quite right ("A right one here") and they then summoned a motorcar to take me on a most comfortable and smooth drive to a large building. I appear in front of my very old and dear friend Lord Chief Justice Shoveha'penny whose attractive wife Diana is so good with flowers, tomorrow afternoon, and from there to the Scrubs at Wormwood for an indefinite period. Bliss!

MARTIN AMIS

The possibility that Iraq will soon have nuclear weapons could have chilling consequences for the world. It is up to writers who have the power to articulate the unimaginable to stress the urgency of the situation, to pick words of sufficient terror to show that nuclear weapons are the exploding turds of our age, that a nuke-turd is like a liquefied-biro in the top pocket of a beige suit, probably three-piece, that the aftermath of nuclear collar-hoist will be more serious than anything we have so far encountered, like a gob of snot-phlegm — phlot? snegm? — on a shiny kitchen surface, or an ear-glob in a plate of vichyssoise, which is chilling; chilling at the moment in fact: I'm having it for lunch with croutons after tennis with Barnesy.

Tennis with Barnesy is, as you know, a regular fixture of my afternoons. Here's a rundown of my morning:

8.00: Have breakfast with my kids. Worry about them being nuked before lunch. At least they weren't in the Holocaust. Or were they? Play with the concept. Walk them to school for a photographer from *Time Out*. Taxi back.

8.45: Arrive at my work sock. "Sock" has become famous as one of the brilliant new words I have invented. It means "flat", but I don't say "flat", I say "sock". I like to think of myself as primarily a comical writer, you see. Arrive at my work "sock" (!) and write three sentences. Ring my agent to tell her that I have written three sentences, immediately. Quickly stick up the dartboard and push the pinball machine centre-stage in preparation.

9.00: Journalist arrives to cross-question me about the three sentences. As he walks in, he notices the pinball-machine and the dartboard, thank god. I say the three sentences have gone pretty well. He wonders if he can ask me what they're about. I say writing three sentences is a bit like dropping a nuke, you never know whether you've hit the target or not, so I'd rather not say.

11.45: Still talking about the three sentences, and about death, which I don't call death in the middle sentence, I call eadth. This is because it's the duty of every novelist living now, in the first half of the 20th century, to reinvent the language. By writing "eadth", I am forcing the reader to confront what it really means.

Suddenly realise that I haven't shown the journalist my snooker cue. Say: "Sorry, lad, time's up, I've got to play a game of snooker with an ordinary person." Journalist obviously impressed, never heard of a writer playing snooker with an ordinary person before. I demonstrate my ear for language "Ordinary persons say 'innit' and 'as such' all the time," I tell him. "Very acute," he says, and I give him time to write it all down with his pus-pen in a scum-pad before showing him the front-hole of the — (!) — sock.

Death is the snare in God's drum-set, the pot-noodle in the scabby puddle, the dandruff in the bouffant, the zit in the plug-hole, the mouldy slice of pig in the two-door saloon fridge.

To lunch at the Caprice nosebag with my mates McEwan and Raine. McEwan is writing a new novel about a man who has sado-masochistic sexual intercourse with a koala and ends it all by biting its head off and hiding it under his hat but he is found out when he goes to somewhere unnamed but which seems very like Buckingham Palace and he is asked to remove all headgear before greeting the Head of State. It's about the psycho/political male/female relationship, and it's very 20th century.

Raine is working on a new poem in which he voices his fears about death today. In one of the most haunting images in 20th Century Literature, he compares death to a "can of Australian peaches in heavy syrup". Over lunch, we discuss this haunting image. "I remember when I saw the corpse of my great-granny," says Raine, tear-pustules bursting through his head-sockets. "I had two vivid impressions. First, that she looked like an Australian canned peach in heavy syrup. Second, that there was snot still in her nose, *even though she was dead*."

"Says a lot about the 20th Century," says McEwan, dabbing his eyes.

"Utterly memorable," I choke.

"Who's for the Creme Caramel?" says the waiter.

Silently, with no conferring, each of us jots down "Creme Caramel" as a suitable shattering image, probably of AIDS.

Choosing names for characters is a complex job for any novelist living in the here and now, the vying demands of swirling realities encroaching on a detumescent actuality to be crystallised in specific codas and propagated in words at once formal and meaningless.

For example, probably my most closely realised character was Kevin Gobfart.

Let me, the author-figure, explain. I had spent weeks trying to create a combination of names that would echo the character's almost apocalyptic obsession with cultural detritus. I had first heard the name "Kevin" about three years ago while watching football on television at the Pinters' in Campden Hill Square, and I had been storing it up for possible use in the future. Then, beating around for a surname, I combined "gob" with "fart" to form "Gobfart", so that the subliminal message of some form of bodily excess might find its way into the intelligent reader's consciousness without detracting from the moment-to-moment realism of the novel.

In my new novel, I have an entirely different main character — more sophisticated, more essentially *humane*, some would argue — and so I have had to think of an entirely different name for him. After hard thought and creative interplay, the name I have come up with is: Trev Belchwilly.

I have been called the poet of the nuclear underclass. Though my own background was "privileged", I have tramped the low-life of Notting Hill and South Kensington in my "foot-socks" (shoes!) for minutes on end, even dropping into pubs and coffee-bars and "rug-rethink-parlours" (that's barbers to you!!!) with a mission to capture the authentic jungle-language of urban decay. So when the gourmandising Jeff T. Fatface eats a Farty-Wankburger in the Shag'n'Piss Diner in the third chapter of my last novel but one, *A Concerned Warning to the Planet* (1983), then burps and says: "Crikey, mate, jolly tasty, 'ave one on me, me old hearty, innit as such, gor bless yer guv", you can be sure that this is the dialogue of today, visionary, disturbing, and chillingly true.

JEFFREY ARCHER

A lot of people ask me at this time of year: "Tell us, Jeffrey, how do you and your devoted wife Mary spend Christmas?" Good question, and it deserves a full reply. As many of you already know, we live in Robert Brook's old Vicarage at Grantchester, and we like to spend the festive season there with our two sons, Jeff (12) and Geoffrey (10). In many ways, they take after their Dad. They're not frightened of competition, they're fond of winning — and why not? — and they have bags of get up and go. Before Christmas Breakfast at 0800 hours, we'll be putting in fifty minutes of Rugby practice, and, straight after a leisurely breakfast, at 0810 hours we'll be putting in some cracker practice for the crackers we'll be having to share with cousins later in the week. With a little concentrated training, it's surprising how often one can win at crackers. Then from 1000 hours, for one hour precisely, we'll have Family Carols, with a prize of £5 for the winner. After Christmas lunch — I do my stuffing well in advance, leaving Christmas free for the family — we play our own impressive list of party games, including "Restaurants", in which each of us pretends to be in a well-known Restaurant while the others close their eyes, and The Truth Game, or Charades as we call it. Come the evening, we traditionally invite a handful of Cabinet Ministers around for a quiet festive bite with their families. This year we are greatly looking forward to entertaining John and Bimbo Gummer with their daughter Margaret, Michael and Popsy Howard with their daughter Margaret, and George and Bunty Younger with their son Margaret. Should be a lot of fun, and if I can give them any advice on the political front, I'll be more than happy.

It's not something I go on about, but I'm a writer of books, and, judging by my latest sales figures — 200 million worldwide — it's not a job I do too badly. A lot of people come up to me and say: "Loved your last bestseller, Jeffrey, but tell me, how on earth did you manage to conjure up such a vivid word-picture of the world of International Jetsetters and Financial Intrigue?" Well, my advice to you all is this: Do Your Research and Get Your Facts Right. I'm setting my next book in Moscow. What does that tell you? Think hard for a minute. Answer: Moscow is not in England. Right. Moscow is in Russia. And what language do the Russians speak? Russian. As I say, in this game you've simply got to do your research. Lazier writers would have had the Moscovians speaking Mosc or Scow or some such language, but I like to Get My Facts Right. Of course, one can't have them speak Russian as such, goodness me no, but one can with the utmost skill convert their speech into a very Russian form of English. This takes a writer's ear. For instance, my first sentence, "You will pay for this with your life!" barked John. "And you will not live to tell the tale, you swine", translates as "You will pay for dis wit your life," barked Ivan, "end you vill not live to tell ze tale, achtung spitfeur." Free advice from Jeffrey Archer! Not a bad Christmas bonus, eh? Cheers to you all from me and my wife Monica!